HYDRA

ADRIANE HOWELL

ADRIANE HOWELL

HYDRA

transit lounge

MELBOURNE, AUSTRALIA
www.transitlounge.com.au

Copyright ©2022 Adriane Howell

First published 2022
Transit Lounge Publishing

Cover and book design: Peter Lo
Cover image: ©Alisa Andrei/ Trevillion Images
Author image: Michel Lawrence

Printed in Australia by McPherson's Printing Group

A cataloguing entry is available from the
National Library of Australia

ISBN: 978-1-925760-98-9

In memory of my grandmothers,
Daphne & Valda

'Isn't it enough to see that a garden is beautiful without having to believe that there are fairies at the bottom of it too?'
– Douglas Adams, *The Hitchhiker's Guide to the Galaxy*

'For whatever we lose (like a you or a me)
it's always ourselves we find in the sea.'
– E.E. Cummings, 'maggie and milly and molly and may'.

B ranches tear her face and legs. She leaps logs, ditches. But damp soil underfoot betrays her route, and rising sun, filtering through the tree line, evaporates her cover. The land has turned from her and soon, she'll be spotted.

Howling dogs – a menacing pack that earlier ripped open her shoulder – shred the silence of an otherwise still morning. They've tasted her and not yet had their fill.

Ahead the wood thins to a splinter of trees. And instinct says there's no choice other than to climb. So she jumps and grips a tree trunk, splitting afresh her shoulder's dog-torn wound. Blood runs down her back; there's no time to tend to it, no time to ponder healthy flesh or any element of the once trusted universal order.

Lying flat on an outstretched bough, she thinks, *If I'm still, I'm invisible. If I'm invisible, I'm nothing but bark and branch and budding leaves; there is no me, separate to this tree.*

The dogs bark, circling below, and a sting – sharp, thick – penetrates her rib cage, chipping bone. She screams, falling heavy to the ground, smacking her spine against a raised tree root. Above her, fighter jets fly west, graffiti on their bellies. And then a man is there, obscuring her sky.

He tells her, she's a wild one. He tells her, she'll be broken.

1

This is not the beginning in narration's traditional sense – things had come before – but if you'll humour me a little, I'll start by speaking of my work at Geoffrey Browne, where we were vultures scavenging remains. After a funeral, in we'd waltz with our Post-it notes: yellow for indexing, green for research, pink for Primas. We'd strip houses to the bones of their walls and clean them of mouldings too, drilling deep, tearing out cartilage to gain the sale items, thicken the catalogue – profiteers of death.

My dear friend Beth said I was too hard on myself, that an auction house was hardly the Serengeti, that I was prone to pessimism and exaggeration – 'miserabilism', she called it. But that wasn't true. I liked the word 'miserabilism'; it felt good rolling around the tongue, proving an appetite for life.

Metaphor aside, the reality is I had no qualms ransacking dead people's houses. It was a thrill finding an object hidden for generations and unearthing its narrative. Who had dusted it, lounged in it, held on to it with a false sense of duty? And for how many decades had it sat in the one room, absorbing years of cheer and anguish that left stains even the most skilled carpenter couldn't sand away?

It was no surprise, then, that I had found a home at Geoffrey Browne Auction House. I was filling an expectation, levelling that deep hole between what excited me and what was a respectable occupation. I was lucky the two soils could meet, though no one's foundations are as solid as they think. Misstep here, landslide there, you'd be amazed what the earth coughs up.

I'll admit, though, my return to work from the holiday was impetuous. Half of me had been swept into the Aegean, and that which remained – the desperate half walking into work that morning – grasped familiarity as if it were a life raft.

I arrived early that late June morning as dealers were unloading their vans in the carpark. It seemed the perfect day to return, as Mondays were for consignments. The morning would be spent haggling with and swearing at dealers, spitting coffee back into cups when outraged by their valuations. I never understood why the best stuff was hidden in the back of their vans, why they insisted on this dance. Each Monday I'd jump on board, rip off a dusty sheet and say, 'Hey, what about this, here? It's worth more than your whole bloody truck.' Well, a specialist would say that; as an administrator I took photos, recorded quotes, pointed out wear and tear. By afternoon, I'd be inside pouring tea for old dears and commending their curations. Such clients rarely admitted it, but I knew they were in the midst of their winter's clean, securing their prized possessions an afterlife. There would be lamps to rewire, Georg Jensen to polish and Charles Blackmans to authenticate. Yet that Monday didn't seem perfect for my return because of the thrill of new stock; it was perfect because everyone would be busy – pull-hair-out, thin-soles-of-shoes busy – and I believed I'd go unnoticed, hidden like a silkworm. No one would think twice about my return; they'd just be grateful for an extra hand to hold the tape measure.

I snuck past the dealers and in through the back door – the alarm had been disarmed. The building smelt as I remembered, earthy like a garden. There was always a fresh bouquet in reception, flowers replaced weekly before full bloom. As our director Lawrence often said, 'We trade in promise, not realisation.' It's not the chair that's for sale, but the idea of sitting in it.

I climbed the stairs to my desk on the second floor in the Mid-Century Modern Department or, as we affectionately called it, Classroom 2B. Geoffrey Browne was housed in a converted school, built in the late 1800s and abandoned a decade later for a larger campus up the road; the auction house had resided in the building ever since. Framed blackboards, hip-height hooks and wide corridors were designed with children in mind, although I'd be lying if I said I ever felt their footprint; they hadn't been there long enough to leave a mark. The three-storey building divided our departments by floor and classroom, giving each its own territory, then uniting us for auctions in the old assembly hall where the public danced to the fall of the hammer. A great administrator knows how to compose this tempo; knows which lots to assign to which antiques. A rare Azerbaijani mafrash followed by a common Provençal mirror stirs the public into a spending frenzy when met by an Archaic Greek ceramic scooped off the ocean floor. It's a symphony of comparisons, an administrator's score, but people are too easily charmed by vocal talent and assign credit to the auctioneer.

I opened the door to Mid-Century. My colleague Fran, usually assigned to lurking in the Collectables Department on the third floor, was sitting at my desk; she welcomed me in what she later clarified was Greek. It was a peculiar trick, cloaked in illusions of camaraderie while suggesting that I shouldn't think myself special, that one needn't spend a month on Greek islands to be considered cultured.

Joke was on her. 'I barely learned a word,' I said.

Her eyes narrowed. She'd exposed herself, tried too hard at playing nonchalant.

Her hands ran along my desk, drawing attention to where she was sitting. I refused to ask why she was parked in my chair or if she'd get up. We adopted a silent stand-off, until she appeared to grow bored and stood, revealing thick black tights and a mismatched brown woollen dress. The garment threatened to split at the breasts, and her hair was swept into a bow. She looked like a girl who'd forgotten she was a woman.

I sat in my warm chair, and she wheeled me in to the desk, her hand firm on my shoulder before her fingers found the Léa Stein brooch adorning the lapel of my blazer. I'd decided on the winking panther brooch the night before for the same reason some women wear red lipstick – confidence – and had spent thirty minutes hunting for it in the unpacked boxes littering my apartment.

Fran twice tapped the plastic cat with her fingernail. 'You always make such bold choices,' she said, sitting on my desk to face me.

It was my fault we'd lost any sense of personal space: I'd been too festive at the last Christmas party and pulled at the stitched bonbons on her holiday-themed skirt. She'd spent the next several months poking and prodding at my clothing to reclaim ground I'd conquered.

'Well,' she said, 'while you were … island hopping, I made some choices of my own.'

I dreaded to think why I should be informed of her choices.

'Now, I know I don't have your extensive education,' a point she often brandished while scrunching her nose as if my degree had a stench, 'but, I thought, if that's what Anja wants, what's stopping me? Why shouldn't I aim high too?' She pushed at my shoulder. 'We could be the next generation of Geoffrey Browne specialists.'

Specialists. The word slid like sewage from her compact mouth. I was never good at poker, a fact I remembered when her smile widened. I reminded myself that the auction house had many specialists of varying expertise and declared my surprise: she'd never mentioned an interest before.

'I didn't have one. But then you were gone, and Lawrence asked me to run Mid-Century's admin. I guess, sitting in your chair every day, I began to think a little like you … *Why does Anja note-take like this? Why does Anja spreadsheet like that?* Perhaps pretending to be you is where I got the idea.' She held her head at an angle as if begging for treats. 'There was even time to refresh some of your more dated documents.'

My keyboard was covered in crumbs and looked sticky from the honey she overloaded her tea with. 'Thank you,' I said.

'No, *thank you.*'

I could have thrown her against the mounted stag antlers, but it was Monday and I was a silkworm, so I just said, 'You're doing extra work today, early hours.' I glanced at my watch. 'I hope Lawrence isn't taking advantage?'

She smirked. And I realised the conversation had shifted to where she'd been guiding it all along. 'I came in at dawn so I'd be prepared, ready to come to the deceased's house with you this afternoon.'

I spasmed. 'But it's mid-century furni—'

'Lawrence invited me, said I could be of some help with smaller pieces – collectables. Rumour has it,' she spoke as if she were divulging news of an illicit affair, 'that there's a complete 1942 bone china Susie Cooper tea set! I'm *dying* to get my hands on it.' Fran uncrossed her legs and jumped from my desk, displaying more of a view than necessary. 'See you at the bus.'

'Fran!'

She spun around.

I knew that to ask would be an admission, a peek inside my cabinet of fear and jealousy, but I needed to know. 'It's collectables that you want to specialise in?'

'Hmm.' She smiled. 'We'll see.'

I could hear her erratic footfall as she ascended the stairs to the kitsch and cobwebs of the third floor – was she skipping? I ran a damp cloth over my keyboard and straightened my brooch. Below my window, dealers squabbled like pigeons.

It wasn't long before the lights in other classrooms flickered on. The Mid-Century Modern Department shared the second floor with the Asian Design and Decorative Art departments. A prestigious floor (unlike the third), but Japanese minimalist furniture was the broken bone in an otherwise consilient skeleton. We at Mid-Century argued that utilitarian pieces crafted between 1930 and 1970, regardless of national origin, were undoubtedly influenced by postwar globalisation and the Bauhaus school of design, and thus should be subjugated to our department. Predictably, Asian Design were big believers in point-of-origin theory and, according to them, the craftsman determined classification, not the period in which they lived. Decorative Art would make a weak claim that the item itself was the determiner, not its context or its creator. *A clock is a clock is a clock*, they would say. Lawrence was often forced to step in and – in true capitalist form, ensuring maximum returns – assigned antiques to departments based on complimentary auction lots and dates.

What I kept to myself was that there is a superior taxonomic method: it's not a question of time, space or matter, but rather one of energy. This was the principle concern of my dissertation at Sotheby's Institute of Art. Unlike my post-grad peers, who wrote their theses on discerning epochs or detecting forgeries, I was concerned with taxonomy. And like many groundbreaking ideas, mine materialised in a dream; while asleep, I conceived a classification of objects based on emotional response. An item is not simply Japanese or 1940s or a clock, it is also aesthetic – demanding an emotion from its observer. Yes, emotions can be subjective, conjured by personal experience (Chapter 3 of the thesis), but they are also universal, evoked through archetypes, collective memory. So, if I were the director of Geoffrey Browne, this imagined clock would find its home in the Department of Ghastly and Grotesque Objects, as there isn't a clock on earth that doesn't count down to its beholder's demise.

But that was Sotheby's and Lawrence was the director of Geoffrey Browne. A year earlier, Mid-Century had lost a 1965

Nakashima desk to Asian Design, and this was still a sore spot. Though, whenever I mentioned it to my colleagues, they'd look confused and take their time recalling the matter. It was the same reaction they had to me that morning when they saw me sitting at my desk. I was lucky it was Monday.

A specialist handed me a bookings sheet. 'Busy morning,' she said with a perfect smile.

After reclaiming my desk, I realised I'd better find Lawrence. I located him in reception with a client: a woman, a few years older than myself, wearing a puffer vest and shifting her weight between each sneakered foot, a small Queen Anne console tucked under her arm. Queen Anne, with its characteristic pad feet, shell carvings and delicate cabriole legs, was a design period so feminine one could imagine menstrual blood seeping from the furniture's joints.

Lawrence kissed the woman on each cheek, then she dashed out the door. He turned to the stairwell and jolted on seeing me, as if I were the ghost of a long-dead school student. The director of Geoffrey Browne, with his polished vowels, kooky socks, expensive suits and orderly procession of pretty fuckboys, had a chic exterior. But it was all moss – underneath he was a red-brick wall with little humour and reactionary politics. Don't get me wrong, Lawrence was a brilliant boss: he wasn't a busybody – squirming when employees discussed their weekends – and valued expertise over charm, as bluffs come unstuck when the hammer falls.

'We need a seamless valuation of today's estate,' he said before remembering it had been a month since he'd last laid eyes on me. He walked over and leant in, giving me a hug that skimmed the fibres of my blazer. 'Welcome back,' he said, retreating from our moment of intimacy. We stood in silence, his eyes to the ground, allowing me a mannered few seconds in which to disclose any personal matters. When it became clear I had no intention of divulging, he clapped his hands. 'Right! The deceased was well regarded. There's an extensive collection to sort and, if we do this properly, we can remind the public that Moderns are best bought at auction – none of this kitsch vintage-store, flea-market business.'

The gravity of his tone didn't befit his cream suit and pink tie. He spoke of his concern for the department – apparently margins were down, a predicament he blamed on 'today's people' (Lawrence never used the words 'youth' or 'young') who were gobbling up the Mid-Century market with not a clue about how to discern an authentic Featherston from its reproduction. Their ill-informed spending was skewing evaluations and driving prices – and Lawrence – to the grave. He was going all out for this estate: a plush marketing campaign, features in newspapers, an article in the *Antiques Gazette*. Any buyer remotely interested in mid-century furniture would read about the auction.

'I've always wanted to be in print,' I said.

He stopped gesticulating and eyed me. 'Anja, is there any reason why you shouldn't be at work today? Any situation or personality with which you will be unable to exude anything other than a professional manner?'

I shook my head.

There was more to say; we both knew it. Instead he handed me the console. 'Store this with the browns.'

The browns were piled on top of each other in a classroom on the third floor. Mahogany, oak, Victorian, Edwardian. Lawrence was stockpiling for a sudden shift to conservatism.

I took the lift to the third floor and carried the console to Classroom 3E. With little storage space left, I made room by tipping the piece upside down, placing it under a desk and piling some nesting tables on top. There were at least five other QA consoles we were never going to sell. I tagged the antique's leg and wished it adieu. If it hadn't been such a twee design I may have felt sorry for it.

Shutting the door, I heard Bertie wheezing and swearing as he trod up the stairs. 'Service! Service!' A regular Monday fixture, he never once thought to use the elevator, and in his sweaty little mitts he'd present some worthless family heirloom for free valuation. He was tolerated at Geoffrey Browne because at every annual patrons' cocktail evening he'd donate the least amount of money possible to ensure his invitation the following year.

Bertie was famous for his gut and his title. His father had arrived in Melbourne in the 30s, after shamings in the motherland. Bertie didn't fall far from the tree and relished tales of 'naughty Daddy' – 'A true libertine,' he'd say with a decaying boyish smile.

I ducked back behind the classroom door, though there was no need: Fran had heard his cry and was skipping down the corridor, her large breasts threatening to burst forth, cartoon birds flying round her head – old Bertie grew an inch. She held his hand as he climbed the last few steps.

'What treasures do you have for me today?' she asked him.

He opened his trouser pocket. 'Ali Baba's cave.'

Fran peeked inside.

He retrieved a King's Medal from the South African War and relayed to Fran its origin: awarded to his great-uncle Albert, Bertie's namesake, 'talented at starving out those buggering Boers'.

Fran held the medal towards the light, caressing it as if it were a piece of Tiffany glass. 'It's precious,' she said, polishing it on her sleeve. Not being a specialist, she couldn't give an official quote, but because Bertie never put anything up for sale no one seemed to mind. She'd pull figures from her bra and off he'd trot with a flu-like afterglow.

True to form, she quoted exorbitantly, and he bowed in mock humility. 'Thank you.'

'No, *thank you*.'

Bertie flushed red. Then, prancing on his toes, he told her of his cavernous house and dire need for a personal archivist.

'That's flattering, Bertie,' Fran was always *flattered*, 'but I have plans for a career here. And you need someone much more experienced than me.'

'Not too experienced.' He kissed her hand and started his prolonged journey down the stairs.

She turned around and saw me watching from behind the door. Everyone treated her like rain in drought, but I knew she'd chosen that hideous dress for one reason. I winked and tipped an imaginary hat.

By midday, whatever insecurities were playing in my mind had melted away. I'd grabbed my toolkit (comprising gloves, camera, Post-its, torch, magnifying glass and tape measures) and spent the morning assisting specialists with their appraisals.

Chessboards, bronze busts, Deco sewing kits. Despite the month abroad, my senses were well tuned, and I was eager to play. I could often pick the specialist's figure in my head before they announced their quote. Antiquing, however, is about judgement calls, and that day I found it difficult to contain myself, once blurting out an unattainable sum for a twentieth-century terrestrial globe. The client was exhilarated, grateful, listing restaurants he would dine at for lunch, but the specialist looked at me in horror, knowing the hammer would fall well below my prediction. What is there to say? I'm generous.

And I'd been right: Monday's rush was perfect for my return. My colleagues barely glanced at my newly tanned skin or the rim of white flesh once hidden by my wedding ring. I imagined that Lawrence had sent out an email requesting a silent front; such things are messy, awkward, and Geoffrey Browne ought to exude stability, professionalism. 'Shelter in an inheritance storm,' Lawrence would say.

After lunch I stood with Lawrence's select few in the carpark, ready to board a minibus to the dead guy's estate. Lawrence liked to give pep talks – he believed it his duty to rally the troops. Standing in front of the bus, he read aloud a colourless speech crafted earlier in the day. It was a familiar script with a few biographical details of the deceased and some final cautionary words. 'Wipe your shoes at the entrance. Be respectful of the bereaved.' He held my gaze. 'And for *God's* sake, don't look too excited.'

My fingers twitched. I climbed onto the bus and sat next to Fran, pushing her ever so slightly against the window.

'I did see you, you know,' she said. 'On High Street. I was

out with my family and didn't want to make a scene. But I saw you.'

This was a typical Fran comment: filled with double meaning, seemingly innocent yet insinuating something darker. I smiled. She was standing her ground, her eyes wide as Susie Cooper saucers.

Lawrence boarded the bus, surveying the two of us before he sat.

There are two types of antiquarians: those who read furniture like books and those who ride them like rollercoasters at a backwater fair. Fran was undoubtedly the latter. I couldn't remain cocooned in silk; if I didn't make specialist before her, I'd die. I'd march myself to the roof of Geoffrey Browne and throw my overlooked body onto the next incoming Queen Anne console. Maybe I'd take Fran with me.

2

When conducting estate auctions, we often found the deceased's house unfit to reflect the furniture's glory. Old dears, much as they do their own bodies, tend to let home maintenance slide and interiors ripen. It was our job to revive these houses for auction, often by carving out a public thoroughfare and removing unsaleables – clothing, Tupperware, photographs – to a warehouse in an industrial part of town. If no amount of staging and flower arranging could redeem the house, the furniture would be shipped to a viewing room at Geoffrey Browne, though I found that whenever furniture was uprooted, specks of magic dust were lost in transit.

Luckily this afternoon's dead guy was childless and only in his forties, so the house was well kept and free of any sentimentals. It was also an ideal mise en scène for a Mid-Century auction, the house having been designed in the late 50s by an influential Australian architect known for his spatial arrangements. From the street it appeared to be a one-storey build, but then artfully descended another floor, hugging the curve of a hill. The façade was sparse: blonde brick, wooden door, a cherry blossom standing on a manicured lawn.

Lawrence led us out of the minibus and down the driveway. I could smell Fran's anti-dandruff shampoo as she skipped by, overtaking me on the path. She was clearly positioning herself: the first employee to spot a Prima took charge of the auction.

Primas are those exceptional items that headline events. They're regarded for their rarity, aesthetic appeal and cultural significance. Like workers in any trade, we have our superstitions, and it's bad luck – vulgar – to discuss monetary value in a Prima's presence. We believe (or tell ourselves we believe) that such items transcend the commercial. Of course, this is all in the hope of conjuring a bidding war.

I could sense an unmasked Prima calling me from inside the house.

Lawrence lifted the knocker, and Miranda (the deceased's PA) opened the door before it fell. She kissed Lawrence's cheeks and, looking relieved, nodded to the rest of us little vultures. She was heavily pregnant and rubbing her stomach with both hands; it was clear we were among the last items to tick off a long list. 'It's been ghastly,' she whispered to Lawrence. 'Miraculous if this baby isn't born with some kind of imprint.'

She guided us down a concrete staircase and into an industrial-style kitchen with floor-to-ceiling windows that looked out onto a wild native garden. The home was sparse, ordered, sober, and yet the garden broke through the restraint with unpredictable cheek, illuminating the deceased's humour. For the first time I could picture Joseph Hiegel, the man behind the interrupted Mid-Century collection.

'This is Mrs Hiegel,' Miranda said, gesturing to Joseph's mother.

She sat across from the breakfast nook, a cashmere cape draped across her shoulders and the back of a chair. Her eyes were glazed, and she barely acknowledged us. We could have burned the world around her and she still would have sat, registering nothing.

It felt crass to have Miranda in the room; to have a mother who had lost her child in close proximity to one vehemently rubbing her unborn's shell. This wasn't the time for babies and inception; this was terminus, where the old and the worn waited to be revived at auction. The bereaved understand this concept – they come to selling with a new vision, one coloured by the lens of the dead. Deep down they want an exchange, however implausible. So they sell off cutlery and crockery, and when the auctioneer announces the clocks, the bereft turn towards the door, hoping for the ultimate trade: chattels for life. But all that passes the threshold are objects as they shift from one owner to the next.

Lawrence indicated that we should spread out – we called it 'hunting'. Fran ran back upstairs to find the study, the place where most people keep their knick-knack collections. As I turned to follow her, Lawrence grabbed my arm. 'Perhaps make Mrs Hiegel a cup of tea,' he said, before retreating to the garden with Miranda to discuss a strategy for the auction. They soon disappeared behind overgrown wattle.

I walked behind the benchtop and flicked on the kettle. 'How do you take it?'

Mrs Hiegel didn't answer. But that didn't matter, because the milk was off – the fridge stank.

She sat facing away from me. Her grey bun was secured with bobby pins. She looked like a ballerina: poised, aloof.

Perhaps the pins were holding more than her hair together; I imagined removing one and watching her crumble like a hollowed egg.

Mourning mothers should not be presented with tea in a Garfield mug. I opened the cupboards, one after another. There was no vessel dignified enough, nothing that spoke to time or sensibility. Until the fifth cupboard, where the complete Susie Cooper tea set glowed holy from its shelf.

The kettle flicked off. I poured in hot water and dunked the tea bag a few times before handing Mrs Hiegel the cup and saucer. Bone china rattled in her light grip.

'May I get you anything else?' I said, glancing at the staircase; Fran was undoubtedly claiming her items. Mrs Hiegel shook her head.

On the wall was a collection of Dora Chapman silkscreen prints: bold, geometric women casting assured and subtle smiles in my direction; I stuck yellow Post-its on the frames. Below the prints, displayed on a teak credenza – possibly 30s French – was a framed photo of a Russian Blue cat, mouth open as if meowing.

'That's Leo,' Mrs Hiegel said, still staring into space.

'Exquisite coat.'

'His parents were show cats.' She gave a smile resembling those in the Chapman prints. 'Leo was born with a crooked tail, and the breeders were going to put him down, but Joseph saved him.'

'A kind act.'

'I doubt he'd have done it for a tabby.'

We looked around the silent room as if Joseph's interior had spoken for him.

'Is Leo with you, now?' I asked.

'He's been rehomed.'

I could hear laughter upstairs.

'How old are you, dear?'

'Thirty. No, thirty-one.'

'Children? Husband?'

'Hayden,' I said, 'and we're trying.' I was surprised by how easy it was to conjure his name and thread it into a lie.

'Good. These days, women leave it too late.' She took her first sip of tea and sucked in air. 'Hot!' she said, brushing imagined creases from her dress. She then told me she'd only had the one child, that her body didn't like Motherhood. Joseph had torn her up inside, made sure there wasn't room for another. 'I regret now,' she said, 'not trying for more.' And then she laughed, as if at a lifelong joke. 'Even when Joseph was alive, he was never enough.'

'No one person is ever enough,' I said.

Our eyes met for the first time. Her irises were grey, as if tears had washed them of all colour. She extended her hand for me to hold, and I thought, *Why not?* When was the last time anyone had offered me a gesture of such acknowledgement, understanding?

We reached for each other, and her cape fell fateful to the ground. I bent to pick it up.

Sleek thin lines, wedged backrest, legs carved from 200-year-old Danish navy oak – the familiar design greeted me from underneath Mrs Hiegel. It was a chair made famous in 1960 for featuring in the first-ever televised presidential debate. JFK and Richard Nixon would go on to navigate the Vietnam War, Soviet missiles and space exploration, but the true visionary that evening was Hans J. Wegner. His creation, known as PP501, spoke of a seamless unity of art, form and craftsmanship. It was more than a chair cradling the bottoms of two future world leaders: it was a design revelation.

The tenons were drilled at right angles to the wood grain and sanded to emphasise the leg joints – the chair was authentic. Its limbs had been sculpted by hand, not machine, indicating an early model, possibly from the 1950 inaugural production line.

On closer inspection, the chair was a shambles: loose cane hung from the seat, needing rethreading; the wood was scratched, and the right back leg had radiant burns, evidence of time spent too close to an open fire.

It didn't make sense. Joseph's interior was considered, refined. It would be out of aesthetic character for him to parade a dilapidated chair in his kitchen nook. PP501 was significant, but it was also the factory's biggest commercial success and a victim of much design piracy. I looked out into the verdant mess of a garden. Unless … unless Joseph had never intended for anyone to sit on it.

I held up my magnifying glass and ducked my head under the seat.

'What on earth are you doing?' Mrs Hiegel asked above me.

Burned into the base were the letters 'H.J.W.' – Wegner's initials.

I paused, looked again and assembled the facts: those initials, the PP Møbler factory materials, high quality craftsmanship … and the rumours. In 1950, a year after PP501's inception, a draughtsman had come to the factory and offered Wegner a handsome sum for his prototype. Never one to esteem his own work, Wegner accepted the legitimate albeit ill-advised transaction, and the chairs were lost forever. Over the years, PP Møbler had attempted to contact the buyer, but he too had disappeared, and the story had fallen into antiquing mythology.

It was near impossible, yet I was surely caressing the legs of Wegner's 1949 prototype. My body tingled. Over oceans and decades the chair had found its way to Joseph Hiegel ... and now to me. If Fran had discovered the chair, it may have been overlooked or *worse*: sent for restoration.

I'd won; I'd found my Prima. I wanted to cry with joy and relief.

Emerging from under the seat, I produced a pink Post-it note and cleared my throat, ready to announce the find.

'I'm afraid not,' Mrs Hiegel said, placing a firm and steady hand on my poised Post-it.

I glanced from her, to the chair, to the crumpled pink paper I was clasping. 'But —'

'The chair isn't for sale. Everything else,' waving her hand in the air, 'but not the chair.'

'Perhaps ... perhaps I could find you another chair to sit on?' *Wegner.*

'I'm perfectly content with this one.'

'Mrs Hiegel,' I said, steadying myself, 'this chair is *significant*. It will fetch you a fortune!' I told her of its history, of the presidential debate, that Wegner's own hand had carved it. I ran my fingers along the wooden legs. 'See, Mrs Hiegel, this chair was carved from the one tree, the one section of wood. It's joined without bolts or nails; there's nothing foreign in there, just mortise, tenons and finger joints – it's pure art!'

Wegner. Wegner. Wegner.

Her lips were tight.

'Its design echoes the Ancient Greek principle of *sophrosyne*: moderation and nothing in excess.'

'You're obviously quite knowledgeable about these things, dear, but I was never moved by history. And, as I said, the chair is not for sale – nor am *I*.'

'But why?! It means nothing to you! If it did, you'd know not to even sit in it!'

Her eyes flashed as she looked down at me. 'Because I have to take something. Because it's not right for a mother to have nothing. His schoolbooks were discarded, his toys are *long* gone.' She poked her chest. 'I was not a sentimental mother,' she said with a note of pride. 'So, I need *something*. Why *this* chair, you ask? Because it's the only thing between me and the ground!'

I looked up at her. Tears welled in her grey eyes, and she fingered a ring on her left hand, presumably from another man in her life, long gone.

'I understand,' I said, and I truly did, but we were vultures – I had to make the call. And while her grief was substantial, I couldn't hold it in my hands. So I uncrossed my legs, shifted my weight back onto my heels and stood, knocking the teacup onto her lap. Hot tea pooled on her white dress. She rose and gasped, smashing the Susie Cooper on the floor. The rush of blood must have been too much for a frail body in mourning, seeing as she moved to sit back down.

But the chair was gone. I had it in my hands. She fell backwards and, as there was nothing to her, I knew it was her coccyx that broke when she began to scream.

AUSTRALIA STATION INTELLIGENCE REPORT
<u>**NAVAL INTELLIGENCE DIVISION**</u>

The Australia Station Intelligence Report is
'SECRET', and its recipients are responsible
for the security of the information contained
therein.

Internal circulation is to be 'BY HAND' of
Officer only. A Transit List is contained in
the back cover.

When not in use the Australia Station
Intelligence Report is to be kept under lock
and key.

Dated: 22 February 1986
Subject: Investigative Report into the HMAS ███
Incidents, 1985
Reference Number: 56947-6740-35IR

Enclosed: Transcripts. The following transcripts were recorded by Investigative Officer Lieutenant Brendan Quartermain on government-provided Dictaphone.*

[ITEM 1]
06:00, 13 September 1985.
Personal Recording: Lieutenant Brendan Quartermain

Three days ago, I was summoned to Canberra by Captain James Alder and Commander Nigel Dane. My superiors briefed me on disturbing activity occurring at training base HMAS ███ in Victoria. It has been suggested that a subversive cadet or group of mid-ranking officers may be responsible. Departing for Melbourne this morning, I am to investigate and report on these incidents.

---

*__A note to the reader:__ The report you have in your hands is counterfeit. It's a replica of an original, which is housed in the Defence Archives in Canberra and can only be accessed via special request. Select Items have been removed from this copy of the report. Through such tampering I hope to have created a paradox: that by blinkering my reader I have carved a transparent path.

3

By the age of seventeen I had moved house eight times. That's not so strange – families often move for work – but my mother didn't have a job and we never left the city. Mum suffered greatly with buyer's remorse. Whenever we ate out, which was often as she thought cooking a waste of time, she'd stare longingly at my plate. '*Anja*,' she'd say, 'always making the right choice. Look at my meal, how *drab*!' Deciding she preferred my dish, she'd order another, handing her plate back to the waiter with a full-teeth smile. 'A present for the alley cats,' she'd say, as if every restaurant in the city were harbouring a family of felines.

She was determined to live life without regrets. So every couple of years, I'd pack my belongings into plastic containers stored under my bed and call removalists. By the time I was in senior school I no longer unpacked my bedroom, knowing full well if Mum saw a house with a spiral staircase or an Edna Walling garden, she'd flee in the night, and there was a chance that in the excitement she'd forget my valuables. With each new house came new clothes and a different brand of cigarettes. For the warehouse loft she wore turtlenecks and rolled Drum. For the manicured terrace she wore pastels and smoked Alpines.

When asked her occupation, she'd reply, 'Property developer', and we both believed it, despite her never knocking down walls or retiling bathrooms. In fact, the mere mention of renovations dropped her into a deep pit of boredom, and nothing could be said or done to rekindle her love for a house once she'd discovered its flaws. Our homes were sold as she had found them and, as I was to discover later, often at a lower price.

Weekends were spent chasing house opens where she brushed against walls and cradled drapes. I once saw her lick a bannister but convinced myself I'd imagined it. When I asked her about it, years later, she told me I didn't feel many things, that she needed to exaggerate to reach me. I think she just liked to exaggerate.

Most children raised by a single parent will, at some point, be confronted with their parent's lover, though I never had to share her with anyone. She was mine and I was secure in the knowledge she had no interest in forming other relationships aside from those with her property acquisitions. My schoolfriends would say it was because she was old, which wasn't true – though she had at least a decade on my classmates' mothers. In actuality, her refusal to partner was to do with the memory of a boy named Edmund. At night she'd stroke my hair. 'Blonde and fine,' she'd say, 'nothing like your mummy's.' I barely knew him, yet I looked more like my father than I did my mother. It was the Danish blood: wild, salty – DNA has a wicked sense of humour. At night when she played with my hair, I knew she was thinking of the boy from across oceans. 'My little Viking,' she'd say to neither me nor him. She'd also say that 'love is for the young'. He was nineteen when they met.

Edmund moved back to Denmark when I was two. My mother would say it was impossible to raise us both; other times, she'd say he was stolen. One night, as our little family slept, there had been a pounding at the door: his parents, come to take him home. He said he would look after me, make sure I never went without. Indeed, each year until my eighteenth birthday, my paternal grandparents sent my mother a neither excessive nor conservative lump sum of child support. But on the night Edmund left our family to rejoin theirs, neither he nor they took a final peep into my nursery.

I don't mention these details to garner sympathy. Up until the age of thirty, despite having rocky foundations, I'd fashioned my own stability: I'd done well at school, attended top-tier universities, undergone an internship at Chiswick Auctions and married well. Mrs Hiegel's accident was regrettable but, you have to understand, I'd been walking the tightrope for some time and my feet had blistered.

It had been three days since Mrs Hiegel broke her coccyx. As first witness to the incident, Lawrence had sent me home on Immediate Stress Leave. I'd spent the time researching Wegner and his chairs, and had put together notes for an article in the *Antiques Gazette*. I even penned a title:

Promising Specialist Discovers Lost Wegner Prototype
Under Mourning Mother's Derrière

The article, in truth, was a distraction. Mrs Hiegel's screams were reverberating in my mind, once even waking me in the dead of night. In dreams I'd confuse smashing china with the shriek emanating from her vocal cords. *SMASH! CRASH! ZASH!* When she opened her mouth, her tongue and teeth would curl around shattered porcelain, and she'd bite into teacups as if they were apples, a defiant look hanging from her face.

My judgement, I admit, had been a little off, though I wasn't convinced the incident was my fault. After all, in the string of events, with actions leading to reactions (stand up, sit down, chair gone), I'd only taken my place in the line. Same as Lawrence, when he'd instructed me to make the tea; or Joseph Hiegel, when he'd failed to stop at the red light; even the unknown dealer had queued up, when he'd sold Joseph the damned chair. Ultimately, it was an endless line of responsibility and blame.

I'd been staring into my morning coffee for an hour when my friend Beth rang. She would call twice a week, and I answered at least seventy-five per cent of the time – well, fifty per cent, if I'm being honest. It wasn't that I didn't enjoy hearing from her; her clarinet voice balanced my equilibrium, melting defensive walls raised in the breaks between our conversations. Yet over the years, I grew irked whenever I saw her name appear on my phone, as what for me was grounding was for her a mere distraction. Beth was in a constant state of distraction. If she was calling it meant she was staring at the oven, stuck in traffic, waiting for her roots to set or, my least favourite circumstance, inconvenienced by the late arrival of another friend. I resented my role as time jester, which wouldn't have been as bad were she focused on our chats, but more often than not she was listening to talkback or fiddling with oven dials. I would be expected to speak through these distractions until her forced inaction ceased – traffic cleared, dye job done – and the conversation drew to a close. And I'd be left juggling the phone.

On this day when Beth rang it was I, however, who needed the distraction, as I had done something completely out of character – or out of my self-perceived character – and try as I might, I couldn't shake Mrs Hiegel's screams from my head. So I answered the phone and was surprised to hear Beth's voice sound steady with concentration. This raised my suspicions, and I asked what she was doing.

'Thinking about you. Let's have dinner – are you free tonight?'

It was the wrong time of the month. While she rang often, we'd only catch up when her period had come; I even put little Bs in my calendar to mark when her blood flowed. Dinner out of cycle was not an occurrence. *She must finally be pregnant*, I thought, but what did it matter? I had no other plans, no family or friends knocking on the door. Since Greece they'd all vanished, fallen through the gap between one life and another – that's what happens when your husband is the social wrangler. It hadn't yet been two weeks since my return, but I knew enough not to expect any calls, that is except from Beth.

'Love to,' I said, and we arranged to meet that evening.

I hung up, and the room grew hushed. If Beth could change her behavioural patterns, why couldn't I? Why should I wallow in the past? I wrote Mrs Hiegel a get-well-soon card and swore to myself I'd spend the next month working overtime to secure consignments.

After making the pledge, I decided a trip to High Street Market would lift my fractured spirit. The market was a labyrinth of forgotten worlds and discarded memories, where I too could become lost and anonymous among china dolls and rotary dial phones. With so much stimuli, the screams couldn't be heard – and one never knows what, or whom, one might find at a market.

Fran wasn't hard to miss: she was wearing a white jumper and cherry-on-top red beret. The beret was not ironic. I watched her from behind an open bookshelf. She fingered watches from a dusty old fruit crate, holding them close to her face and peering at time as it ticked over. What was she assessing – their make, age? Unmoved, careless and without love, she dropped them back into the crate.

I knew little of her life outside of Geoffrey Browne. If she had a private collection of knick-knacks, she never spoke of them. Her hunting was always with the auction house in mind – I hadn't once seen her purchase anything for herself. I tried to imagine her at home, sitting at dinner. What period was the table or the crockery she ate off? With whom did she dine? I couldn't picture her connecting with anyone – family, housemates, lovers, male, female? – and certainly not surrounded by anything resembling beauty. Everything that articulated her taste and passion was off, falsely curated, poorly imitated. She was without discernment, context or history, a fraudulent aesthete haunting me since my first day at Geoffrey Browne.

As she wandered around the china cabinet, it became clear why she was there. It's not uncommon for auction houses to complete sets by merging items from different sources. One can add hundreds to a vintage tea set by spending fifty dollars on a missing component. A free tip for those who inherit Granny's Wedgwood: spend a day completing the set, cause if you don't the buyer will.

Careful not to be seen, I followed her as she weaved in and out of china aisles. She'd undoubtedly spent the last few days coating my keyboard in honey and signing my emails with a smiley face. I wanted to rip the beret off her head (maybe even take a few hairs with it). I could imagine her at work the next day, telling stories of hat-thieving Anja who once so tightly grasped the game of life.

As if in a dream, I turned the corner and she was gone. No sign of her red beret bobbing between stalls.

That night, as was tradition, Beth picked the restaurant, a decision usually based on who stocked her family's vintage or whose wine list she was attempting to annex. I was surprised, then, to find myself at a tapas restaurant specialising in Spanish wines; she never relished dinner that didn't involve some level of networking. Something was off.

She flew into the restaurant typically late and brought with her the freezing night air. We embraced with me still seated, she arched over me from behind like a warm and heavy coat. Ignoring the menu, she took charge of ordering, rolling her wrist in the air as she described the smoke and bite of a particular jamón to the waiter. She'd been here before.

'I've ordered us a Russian roulette,' she whispered to me, leaning into the table. 'Pardrón peppers – one in ten is extra spicy, a real kick in the balls!'

If we weren't there to sell wines, we must be celebrating. She was definitely pregnant.

I suddenly felt self-conscious, as if my reaction to the news would set a tone for the next twenty years of friendship. Would she find it reassuring that I'd guessed the little secret, that her thoughts were never masked long from mine? Or should I declare shock, allow her the triumph of surprise?

The waiter returned with our peppers, and Beth ordered a bottle of Tempranillo.

'I'm worried about you,' she said.

Did she know Mrs Hiegel? Had Beth's grape vines reached into the world of antiques?

Taking my hand in hers, she told me there was a fix. She could organise a dinner, us four, casual, at her place. She was sure I'd been misunderstood. It was easy, she said, to misconstrue my intentions.

It took me a moment to realise she was talking about my marriage.

She let go of my hand and rubbed at the stem of her wineglass. It was clear – I'd disoriented her. Beth had known Hayden and me since school, had been our maid of honour: a one-off duty she'd warped into a lifelong obligation.

'You had all these plans,' she said, 'and for whatever reason – sunstroke, island fever – your future is now … uprooted. It's all so … so *rash*.' She took a sip of wine and nodded to the waiter to pour. 'I'm sure we can untie this knot.'

I thought it best not to mention my few days off work and the other unfortunate incident in which I'd found myself entangled.

'I mean, who has the energy to start again?' she said. 'I'm sure Hayden feels the same way.'

'So you're not pregnant?'

'What? *No!* The doctors say my hormones are balancing, so the drugs are working.' She pointed at her wineglass. 'Don't. Tell. Miles.'

It was a sentence I'd heard many times, when she would effortlessly down two bottles of red and distribute business cards to half the restaurant.

'Speaking of Miles,' she said, 'he did mention that Hayden *may* want a clean break … and, in that case, I've a friend, well, a colleague —'

'Beth.'

'Okay, fair. It's just – you're all alone. I'm sorry, but it's true. And I know you want kids, or at least you say you do, and I'll always be there – I'm here now – but you need more than me, like an insurance policy … It is what you eventually want, family?'

I nodded.

'Okay, great.' She sat back in her chair, content we were on the same path. 'How's work?'

'Good.'

'Great.'

At home awaiting me was an email from Lawrence, inviting me to a disciplinary hearing. This was the most popular I'd been in days.

Tomorrow, 6pm, can you make it?

Yes, I'd love to.

4

Setting myself on a redemptive path had scattered the misgivings playing in my mind. My dreams that night were free from screams and smashing teacups, and the dread I had felt that week upon waking was nowhere to be found.

I rolled up the bedroom blind. Morning light seeped in, stilted by the adjacent high-rise. My neighbour across the way had hung some washing on her balcony; if I'd wanted to, I could have reached across the fifteen-storey chasm and snatched her knickers off the line. The restful night had made me silly, or perhaps it was the excitement of a sit-down with Lawrence. Of course, I'd have to apologise – I wanted to! – but this was also an opportunity: he rarely granted formal meetings. I'd heard colleagues complain about it. They'd say, 'Lawrence, let's meet to discuss X', and he would say, 'What about X?' My unprepared colleagues would find themselves in the midst of a meeting, their proposals half-baked then disregarded.

But I'd been granted time and had an idea, a balm to ease Lawrence's woes. Although Fran could perhaps replicate my admin work, she hadn't a clue about taxonomy. I'd explain to Lawrence that by evolving the departments, stripping objects to their essential meanings, we could abate Mid-Century's fiscal stress and revolutionise the industry. Those posturing, lacking sensibility, would be exposed and out the door.

I flicked on the kettle. My bare feet stuck to grime on the laminate floor that had been there since I'd moved in near two weeks prior. My swaying high-rise with its plywood cabinetry and loose fixtures was popular with international students and those between lives. I'd found the place online while at a taverna in Athens and had driven there straight from the airport upon landing.

I poured two spoonfuls of loose-leaf tea into a George IV silver pot that had belonged to my grandmother. My mother's parents had died before I was born, my grandmother in childbirth to an uncle who had also slipped from this world. My mother was eight at the time and seldom spoke of them. My grandfather had been a chemist, a compounder. He never remarried and, for all my mother knew, didn't even date, mostly staying at the pharmacy, pounding away – until they found him face down in his mortar and pestle. It occurred to me, rubbing the teapot like a genie lamp, that other than these details I knew nothing of them. With my mother's death their history, mannerisms and dreams had vanished. Teapots, I decided, were connected to storytelling, belonging to the Department of Once Upon a Time.

Cradling the sterling silver, I turned and saw myself in the moon-like mirror of my mother's Deco dresser: three generations caught in reflection. Twice or thrice when modelling in the mirror, I'd caught glimpses of my mother next to me, painting her lips, spraying perfume. It was as if her image had been trapped in the frame, nestled between glass and mercury coating. This, though, was mostly fanciful, and try as I might on those days of desperate loneliness, I was never able to rattle her into the reflection, no matter how much lipstick I'd apply or how many glasses of wine I'd down.

It was because of this reflection that I'd kept the dresser when I'd purposely discarded most of her other belongings. While the other items had placed visions of her in my mind, this one caught her in my line of sight. It was not active remembrance but passive witnessing – of a ghost, frankly, without all the haunting nonsense. Whether she was there or not, it didn't matter; I took pleasure in knowing that something cascaded over the boundaries of my own understanding, leaving me bewildered and freefalling – which, I appreciate, is not a feeling most people enjoy. Mirrors, then, are to be housed in the Department of Unexplained Phenomena.

When I arrived for my hearing at Geoffrey Browne, most people had gone home for the evening, though not Fran. Typical of her to make the most of her time while I was away. I eyed her as I walked towards the meeting room, and she held my gaze.

Lawrence was sitting next to Ian from HR at the oval table. I sat opposite them, and Ian poured me a glass of water. I'd rarely seen him, let alone had anything to do with him. His office was a small space under the staircase where schoolchildren had long ago hung their bags and blazers. I'd stepped inside once, on joining Geoffrey Browne, and noted a corn-chip smell. Ian ate his meals alone and never showed an interest in antiques. He was a pale, unkempt man who hadn't a hint of aesthetic sensibility or pleasure and may as well have worked HR in a nursing home or abattoir.

But that evening he was an Ian I'd never seen before: confident, well rehearsed, with cheeky eyes – as if he'd been waiting for this moment his entire career.

'Let's begin,' he said, 'with the formalities.'

I nearly swooned at his new-found self-possession.

'Firstly, Anja, I'm required to inform you that you are permitted a support person. Is there anyone you would like to invite? Friend, colleague … lawyer, perhaps?'

I scanned my memory for a support person: Beth – already perturbed. A lawyer – too dramatic. Hayden – for him to gloat? Fran – ridiculous! Mum – dead!

'No, thank you. I decline.'

'Formally declined,' Ian said, jotting something down and turning to Lawrence.

My director's head was resting in his hands. He was wearing a red shirt and red tie that highlighted the bags under his eyes. He stared at me and then at Ian.

'It's your turn,' Ian whispered to him.

'Well.' Lawrence sat upright, drumming his fingers on the table. 'Let's see —'

'First off,' I said, 'I am beyond sorry for what happened to Mrs Hiegel, and I wish her a speedy recovery.' My heart raced. 'But, I must say, how was I to know she would fall back onto the chair?' I took a sip of water. 'I'd also like to take this opport—'

'Anja,' Lawrence said, his hand raised. 'I'm happy to report Mrs Hiegel has left the hospital and has decided, thankfully, to continue with the auction – and not to press charges. You have, however, put us in an unprecedented situation.'

'I appreciate that and —'

'The code of conduct was broken. Obliterated.'

'Not intentionally.'

'Even if that is the case,' he pressed his palms into his eyelids, 'we have to address other allegations made against you.'

'Allegations! By whom?'

'At this stage,' Ian interjected, 'we aren't at liberty to say who the accuser, or should I say, "alligator" is.' He beamed. 'You may, however, be able to decipher their identity from the specificity of the allegations.'

I turned to Lawrence. 'Well?'

He bit the inside of his cheek. Ian's pen shook in anticipation.

'We have received complaints,' Lawrence said, 'from a fellow member of staff … regarding comments. Inappropriate in nature.'

'Inappropriate?'

'In respect to their personal life.'

My throat tightened. 'I think, you'll find, that I am, in fact, rather professional and – like you – take little to no interest in my colleagues' personal lives.'

Lawrence rolled his eyes. 'Comments of a sexual nature.'

Ian shrank into his chair, his newfound confidence dissolving with each syllable: *sex-u-al*.

'A colleague,' Lawrence continued, 'believes you are harassing them; making degrading remarks about their clothing and body, and their interactions with clients. They've also spotted you following them outside of office hours … although, to be fair, I acknowledge these occurrences may have been coincidental.'

That little bitch.

'As such, in conjunction with pushing Mrs Hiegel off of her chair —'

'She fell backwards!'

'We have no choice, Anja.'

Ian rose and slid an indenture under my nose. He took a pen and, when I didn't move, placed it gently in my hand. 'Sign here.'

My throat was barely letting in air, and large sobs fell onto the page. 'But I have plans for working late,' I squeaked, 'for pulling in consignments. I discovered a taxonomy and please, I, I want to be a specialist.'

'I know it's been a hard month,' Lawrence said, his voice soft, 'but we can't have you working at Geoffrey Browne. You're too volatile. We project confidence and order at a time when people most need it. You're simply not aligned with such principles.'

'We asked you here after work hours,' Ian offered, 'so that you wouldn't have to see anyone. We thought this would be in your best interest.'

'Thank you?'

He nodded with dignity.

'I'm sorry, Anja,' Lawrence said, 'you'll need to clear out your desk.'

I was numb, gasping quietly. Years of work, research, ambition, amounted to nothing, void. Abstracts floating further and further out of reach into a life no longer mine.

I drifted down the hall towards my desk, Ian by my side. Fran was nowhere to be seen, though truth be told I may not have recognised her – she could have been a standing lamp or coathanger.

There was nothing at my desk I wanted. Not plants, nor pens. My computer wasn't corrupted with personal files; I had no photos or trophies. The only adornment was an office-owned antique hole puncher, cast iron with a gold leaver shaped as a lion's head. I picked it up, dangling it above my bag. Ian was barely looking at me, apparently fascinated with his shoelaces. Perhaps the hole puncher was too heavy or my crimes too exposed, but I thought twice and put it back. *Do I go to the roof and jump, end it all?* A pile of biscuit crumbs surrounded my keyboard.

I picked up the lion's head and shoved it into my bag.

I arrived at HMAS ███ in the late morning. The base is an hour's drive south of Melbourne. It's cut from the land in the shape of a horseshoe with two peninsulas surrounding a marine inlet and a three-kilometre strait. From the public road there's little to see: thick shrubs, moonah trees, the occasional glimpse of a lake in the distance.

The main gate is patrolled, and the sailor on duty requested identification when I drove up. I've been told, however, there are multiple entrances that do not require any sign-in; these are primarily on the Eastern Peninsula, around the golf course and the residential community. The township is located at the head of the inlet. It's a typical centre: bank, cinema, post office, kindergarten. The strait is guarded and used exclusively for docking naval ships and submarines. It'd be near impossible for an unmarked vessel to approach.

The restricted area, and location of concern, is the Western Peninsula: a wetlands reserve of 1000 hectares, spotted with research facilities and a shooting complex. I'm told it's the habitat to various wildlife and a few endangered species — in particular, a long-toothed bandicoot.

On arrival I was met by Commanding Officer Captain Glen Morrissey. We drank coffee in his office as he familiarised me with the base's facilities, geography, main order of business — all the details I mentioned earlier. He then recapped the incidents described by Commander Dane and Captain Alder.

Captain Morrissey measures his sugar by levelling two teaspoons with his little finger, so I can't imagine that much occurs on base without his knowledge. I asked him if my interviews might begin with him, but he declined, stating that he didn't see the point. He told me not to skip ahead. The stories, he said, didn't begin with him, and if they should lead to him, only then would he be happy for us to officially sit down together. On finishing his coffee, he called in Petty Officer Matthew Gibbs to direct me to my quarters.

Gibbs took the wheel of my hire car, driving us out the main entrance and back onto the public road. When I asked why we were leaving the base, he explained that there was no direct vehicle access to my accommodation — I was to be housed in a cottage in the middle of the wetlands reserve. The road only goes so far in, Gibbs told me, and it's long been overgrown, but there's another security checkpoint from the public road. One sailor and a flimsy farm gate guard this access point. The gate opens to a thin stretch of dirt cutting through the wetlands and tracking west towards the sea. It leads to cleared bush and the cottage, which he said was the first building erected when the government bought the land in 1911.

He unlocked my quarters and pointed out the radio, CD player, television and two-way transmitter to base, all the amenities needed to keep me from feeling isolated. But the cottage is too far, for my liking, from the township. When investigating in-house, I like to live among the community — blend in, a friendly face. After all, cases often crack when neighbours drop by for tea. When I queried Gibbs on my remote location, he told me that officer accommodation was fully booked due to a visiting English fleet and that I could raise the issue with the Captain if I so desired.

Captain Morrissey appears to have stowed me away. It's disappointing, but at least the cottage has a pleasant view and a wooden ladder leading down the rocky cliff to a private beach.

Back outside, Gibbs pointed to a near-overgrown path in the bush and said that the five-kilometre track led to the township. I had more queries but it's unwise to challenge personnel so early in an investigation, and besides, Gibbs was swallowed by the bush before I had time to ask my next question.

[ITEM 3]
17:00, 13 September 1985.
Recording: Two-way Transmitter between Base & Cottage.

[inaudible], come in? Over … Lieutenant Quartermain? Over.

This is Quartermain. Over.

Lieutenant, this is Chief Cook Dixon. I've been advised that you will not be eating in the Captain's Dining Room this evening. I'll have an officer bring you a tray. Would you prefer the lamb chops or the tuna mornay? Over.

This is news to me, Dixon, who advised? Over.

The Captain, Sir. Over … Lieutenant? … Lieutenant, would you prefer the lamb chops or the fish mornay? Over.

Ah, lamb. Over.

Copy that, and to drink, Sir? Over.

Wine. Red. Over.

I'll send a bottle. You'll find cereal in the cupboard and milk in the fridge. Have a good night, Lieutenant. Over.

Out.

5

I'd dragged my weary body up and down the freezing High Street and to every antique dealer in the city. But their faces grew like cuckoo clocks – angled and suspicious – when they read the name atop my CV. Rumour spreads like mites to wood, and I was ready for the sawmill.

I learned to avoid social gatherings and the few friends I had left – avoiding pity and the inevitable confusion my story brought to people's faces. *It was all a mistake*, I wanted to scream, *a series of unfortunate events, of misunderstandings and potential sabotage*. Yet few looked at me the same once I mentioned being haunted by the sound of smashing china, which had once again entered my dreams.

My world grew smaller than I imagined possible and, for the first time in an otherwise exemplary life, I could see my unremarkable future, without career, family or friends. And I foresaw myself half eaten by alley cats in the modern high-rise before putrid flesh alerted my student neighbour.

Beth was my only support, never judging or criticising. She could tell I was in disgrace and that a lecture wouldn't change a thing. She was, however, quieter than usual, and in these periods of silence she'd furrow her forehead as if she were solving some great riddle. If she was trying to untangle my life, I was glad for the help.

With little to do I read my thesis over and over, speaking the title aloud and backwards, jumbling words, mixing verb with noun:

'Distilling Antiques: The Classification of Objects through Essence and Archetype'

'Classifying Antiques: Distilled Objects through Essence and Archetype'

'Objects: Distilled Antiques, Essence and Archetype'

'Essence and Archetype Distilled into Objects'

'Distilled Essence into Object Archetypes'

'Antique Essence'

'Distilled'

My ruinous chair: core to Modernism, cloaked in mystery and now a symbol of impairment – Mrs Hiegel's, mine – *hurl* it to the Department of Dysfunction.

It could be worse, I told myself. *I could be broke*. My mother had left a little money, I hadn't been so pitiful as to ask anything of Hayden, and I estimated that if I lived frugally, I could survive a decade without working. By forty, I'd be completely unemployable but I might also be dead.

A month into exile, mostly to cure boredom, I opened two online accounts: one for buying, the other selling. They offered a steady albeit low income, as while my taste and perception were as finely tuned as ever, the market for antiques was dismal. I found myself selling trite mock Memphis – and, god help me, collectables! My stomach cramped whenever I pressed 'purchase' on a plastic knick-knack.

At night I'd down a bottle of red by the electric heater and scroll pages of Geoffrey Browne's online catalogue. The Joseph Hiegel Collection was going ahead in November; those interested in a private viewing were to contact Fran. Many times I'd hover my mouse over her email address, speaking out loud the barrage of questions I'd have liked to hound her with: *If the auction house were burning would you save the Ruhlmann or the Rizzo? The Russian bureau stamped on the back or stamped in a drawer?*

And then one night, two months into my exile, a question stuck like bile in my throat, and I immediately knew her smug answer and the solution to my unemployment.

I poured another glass of red. Top of Geoffrey Browne's webpage was a button marked 'login'. In recent years, the auction house had evolved to allow online bidding, capitalising on interest from foreign markets and a convenience-consumed society. If you ask me, sales were increased at the expense of auction-day buzz, the room losing its sway and sweat to the digital ether. The shift in times also meant that staff had our own online accounts where we could access catalogues, running sheets, contact lists. 'Our', 'we' – I realised I'd have to adjust my vocab.

A red-wine gaze guided my unsteady fingers. *Click.* Ian from HR had been staring at his shoelaces too long; I still had access to it all. I got what I needed and got out.

Bertie's bluestone manor was the last house on a long street lined with pine trees. Behind the house was a seaside golf course, of which Bertie – he had informed me – was an honorary member. Leading to his property were equally large though contemporary homes with shameless windows and alfresco kitchens. These properties had originally formed part of his estate, which had been subdivided in '85 when a middle-aged Bertie realised he no longer had the resources nor family hands to run the paddocks as a dairy farm.

The home was an hour's drive from the city, though it felt a world away. I parked on Bertie's drive and opened my car window, letting the salt breeze tangle my hair. My winter's ostracism had ended. It was the first day of spring. Felicitous, I thought, for a new life, new beginning. I closed my eyes and breathed in that cosy, finite time between having a new job and executing the tasks. I'd do the job for six months, get a reference, get out, starting afresh with a no-longer-tainted CV. It wouldn't be long before my return to the world of commercial antiques.

This was a Lawrence-like pep talk, but it stopped me gripping the wheel and got me out of the car.

I'd gone with a less formal look than I had in the office: I wore a white silk blouse and olive green pants cut in a 40s style that was tailored at the waist with a sensible flare at the hip. I'd kept my shoes flat, as I'd learned long ago that anything higher than a kitten heel wasn't conducive to lifting and shifting furniture. The pants, though, were tighter than usual, and my skin had lost its glorious Aegean tan. I was suddenly ashamed of my appearance.

I knocked and waited. Curtains fluttered in a nearby bay window; someone – I knew who – was hidden behind them.

When Bertie opened the door, it took him a moment to recognise me. Disappointment fell upon his face. Perhaps he'd confused me with another Geoffrey Browne girl, and I didn't blame him; I'd never once shown him any attention, never once humoured his garbled stories or tedious belongings. Yet here I was, his enthusiastic new employee.

'For archiving?' he said, as if I were a mistake, a coincidence, while he awaited the fresh-faced Fran.

I confirmed this, and that familiar boyish smile crept across his face. 'How special I feel,' he said, 'you coming all this way, just for me.'

I told him how I'd long admired his heirlooms, how it was a travesty they weren't chronicled.

He raised his finger to silence me. 'Let us chatter in the library.'

I followed him down a passage into the depths of his house. The rooms either side were dark and dank, the curtains drawn. The spaces appeared lifeless, unused for decades. The air had a faint odour of molasses, and I thought of Hansel and Gretel tearing through the gingerbread house. Bertie shuffled ahead, breathing heavily and turning around often, as if to make sure I was still there.

Along the passage was an Edwardian side table coated in dust. A bronze mermaid statue, no bigger than my palm, stood alone dressed in its own dust jacket. When I was fourteen, my father – having been absent for twelve years – sent me a postcard of the Little Mermaid statue in Copenhagen, along with a photo of my new baby sister. I received the same mermaid postcard when I was sixteen, that time with a photo of my baby brother. I had no further contact with Edmund until I was eighteen and travelling in Europe. Even then, he and his family made it clear that I was only to stay the weekend; the children's schedule couldn't be thrown out, and St John's Eve was fast approaching, which meant they would be vacationing on the isle of Bornholm. I was not invited to Bornholm. During our two dinners together, both of which nights we ate meatballs, his wife Lina did most of the talking. She liked to talk about plans: did I have any? How long was I to stay in Europe? Did all Australians struggle with foreign languages? Did I ever plan to learn one? The day I left Denmark, Edmund paid for my train fare and wished me luck. I phoned seven years later when I was living in London, but he never phoned me back. Glancing through Bertie's forlorn rooms and possessions, I realised we were both alone in the world. This was the nugget of empathy I needed to perform my job.

On the golf-course side of the house, the rooms began to warm as sunlight stretched through open curtains. The library that Bertie had guided me to was a makeshift TV room for one, with a lone leather armchair and android television on a wheeled trolley. A petite tray table with a plate of lamingtons stood next to the chair. The library walls were lined with hardcover books and, for a moment, I felt like Belle in the Beast's castle.

Bertie ushered me to sit. The arms of the chair were caked with food. He lifted the plate of lamingtons and put them under my nose, heralding the skill of the local baker. I popped one into my mouth, and he took the plate away, cradling it while watching me eat. Jam coated my tongue, reminding me of football matches, grandparents I'd never met and school fetes.

'Good?' he asked, eyes alight.

I considered the possibility that Bertie was the baker and that I was being drugged, but I shooed the thought from my mind. 'Thank you for seeing me,' I said between mouthfuls of nostalgia. 'I believe you are in need of an archivist?' I swallowed the last bite and licked my fingers.

He seemed to like that, as he rocked up and down on his toes. 'As you can see,' he said, moving his arms to draw in the room and indeed the estate, 'I'm burdened. The spoils of history, my dear.' He seemed to blush. 'I need to bring an order to these trappings.' He wanted cue cards of facts for each item. He wanted to 'empower' his guests with 'knowledge' and an understanding of an object's 'significance'. He wanted to point at a piece and be able to claim it as circa X, belonging to great-granddaddy Y, travelling from India or Kenya or wherever the thing came from. 'When everyone is dead,' he told me, 'the past tends to fade.'

'You need cataloguing,' I said.

'And the Dewey System – these books warrant professional treatment.'

'I'm not a trained librarian.' I paused. 'But I can suggest a radical taxoni—'

'The ladder,' he blurted. 'Climb it. Show me what you've got.'

Was this a trial, a challenge? I went towards the ladder that hung from the bookshelves and slid along the wall, hinged to an iron rod that locked on to a shelf. There was an indent in the floorboards where the ladder's wheels traversed, perhaps for a hundred years. I locked the ladder into place and climbed until I was face to face with the highest shelf. It was clear that Bertie never read these texts let alone dusted around them; pages were badly foxed, and the books were stuck to one another. Their glue had dissolved, separating bound pages from their covers, and cobwebs had built up between the bindings and spines.

The mark on the floorboards was not Bertie's doing.

In close proximity to the books, the air was damp, warm, heavy. I soon realised the extra heat was radiating from Bertie. Silent as a carnivore he'd crept under me, standing directly between the ladder and the shelves. *To hell with him*, I thought. *If he wants to spend his time ogling me, what do I care?* I read the titles of a collection of Churchill's writings: *Arms and the Covenant, The River War, Great Contemporaries*. Bertie edged under my shirt, sprightlier than I'd imagined. One swift move and he was tweaking my nipples. I stared at a chaise longue covered in old newspapers in the corner of the room. I knew it was eighteenth-century Italian but, if asked, what would I offer as evidence? Rococo foliate embellishments, boisterous brocade?

Bertie pulled at me like he was milking a cow. I could have yelled and kicked and done all the things that I thought a good feminist would do – that I'd thought I would do. In truth, aside from some slight discomfort, I barely cared; his hands were so soft. Beth would have been appalled by my passivity, but who was she to judge? I wanted to work with antiques, and if this was the price –

Bertie was hooting, like an owl.

And then it started, I couldn't help it: the laughing. Full body laughing. I covered my mouth with both hands and tried not to convulse, but all sense was gone and I was nothing aside from roaring cords and a spasming diaphragm.

The tweaking stopped.

'No, please,' I said, nearly falling off the ladder, 'continue.'

Bertie's hands fell to his sides, and he stood staring into space until my laughter subsided. Then, like a sulking child destroying a favourite toy, he said, 'I think I'll sell the lot.' Vexed at the position I'd apparently forced him into, he grew red and defiant and raised his eyes to mine. 'It's worth a fortune, you know,' he said, 'according to that charming girl at Geoffrey Browne.'

6

The confines in which I'd once functioned in the world – rules and schema: moral, social, aesthetic, conceptual-self – had eroded into the Aegean. Once again unemployed, I sat in my car outside Bertie's house, unable to move, change the radio station or even decide where to drive next. I was detached and floating above my body. Yet at the same time, each limb, each neuron was purring. *This must be shock*, I thought. But it wasn't from violation or debasement. It was from realising the whole thing was a lie: the sea had consumed my cage, and I'd become unrecognisable. Still, I was alive.

China smashed – perhaps that was only Bertie inside the house, destroying some of his inheritance.

I managed to drive out of the property, away from the ocean and deep into the heart of the peninsula, the gully, where air was damp and soil rich. Shaded by evergreens, the road twisted upon itself, traversing the natural curve of the landscape. I drove over streams and through mist. I drove past vineyards and breweries, restaurants and galleries: land – unlike myself – dotted with purpose.

Just as dank air began to weigh on me, I emerged on the other side of the gully where once more I could smell the

ocean. I'd turned left and right with no regard to destination
and found myself on a straight deserted road named Hill Pass.
To my left were empty paddocks and the occasional eucalypt;
to my right was built-up marshland with dense scrub and little
visibility. For a fleeting moment I saw a silver lake with cranes
and pelicans, but soon lost sight of it. Along the border of the
marshland was a wire fence, and every thirty or so metres a
yellow tin sign appeared.

> Commonwealth of Australia
> Department of Defence
>
> TRESPASSING AND / OR SHOOTING
> IS PROHIBITED
>
> TRESPASSING UPON OR SHOOTING OVER THIS
> LAND IS A PUNISHABLE OFFENCE
>
> Crimes Act 1914 (Cwth)
> Defence Act 1903 (Cwth)

The faster I drove, the quicker the signs appeared, like
guardian angels tracking the side of my car. I was swaddled in
their beat, tapping my hand on the wheel whenever I passed
one.

Tap. One, two, three. Tap. One, two, three. Tap. One,
two, three. [ ]

A missed beat. Had the sign been yanked? Looking in
my rear-vision, I could see that where the sign should have
been, the fence gave way to a narrow dirt path leading into the
marshland. It was a near imperceptible break in the fence, and
one not paying attention to the signs may not have noticed the
sly road. At this marshland entrance I could make out another
sign, made from cardboard and staked into the ground, but I

was too far away to read the lettering. I spun the car around and drove back towards the path.

I can't say exactly what made me turn around. 'Directionlessness' was the excuse I used at the time. Now, though, I think I may have been motivated by the signs – they were taunting me, begging me to disobey, to tiptoe over the wire fence.

The staked cardboard sign read: 'FOR SALE. Commonwealth Land and Dwelling'. A sign below, printed on laminated A4 paper and attached below, read: 'Open Inspection'. The metal farm gate was propped open by a small, welcoming boulder.

I drove down the narrow dirt path. The shrub thicket on either side – drooping she-oaks and native brambles – was dense and canopied the road, allowing little sun to break through. The wire fence and yellow signs continued either side of me, popping up every thirty or so metres in case I'd forgotten not to stray from my path. Not that one could trespass: the flora was so thick and hostile, only a machete could clear tracks.

After a few minutes I arrived at a clearing. The crescent-shaped land stretched about a hectare, was nuzzled by scrub and spilled out over a small cliff with a rocky shore below. The place felt known to me, as if from a painting or another life. The land was dotted with twisted moonahs, a couple of which lay uprooted and skeletal on the ground, but was otherwise barren save for some overgrown wallaby grass and coastal wattle. Facing the ocean was an early 1900s, single-fronted weatherboard worker's cottage with a rusty corrugated roof and worn brick chimney. Three wooden steps led up to a rickety verandah and a waving woman in a cobalt-blue suit.

She welcomed me with the smile of a long-lost friend and

introduced herself as Davina. 'First visitor all week,' she said. 'I was beginning to think seafront property had gone out of style.' Had she been waiting there all week? Handing me a brochure, she winked a blue-shadowed eye and swept out her manicured hand, directing my attention to the ocean. She then tottered towards the cliff in six-inch heels, while I jogged to catch up. We stood on the precipice of a five-metre drop. There was no sand below, only boulders and lapping water. She gesticulated again, bangles clinking together. 'Imagine.' She spoke of summer nights, deckchairs, cheese and wine for two. There was a man in this fantasy – a 'hubby' – and he valiantly swatted at mosquitoes buzzing round my cardigan. I could see how taken Davina was with this fantasy, her head tilted in contemplation, and I wondered how many people she had tried to sell such stories to.

The rocks below looked slippery, and I couldn't see a ladder. 'How do I get down to the water?'

She seemed perplexed, as if the characters in her head preferred not to swim. 'I guess you could climb. Though there's a public beach only three kilometres away. Turn left —'

'You can't swim here?'

She sighed and rushed a speech, as if bored of going through it. 'Technically, no, the beach stretch belongs to base – the nearby naval base. They're the seller. This clearing was carved from their nature reserve. It *was* the doctor's residence until the 70s but has mostly been unused since then. Long ago there was a path to the base from here.' She pointed at the scrub. 'Somewhere.'

I gazed out at the tantalising ocean, a body of water only to be marvelled at and never to meet the dip of a toe.

'Sailors can use it,' she said, 'but not the public.'

I must have seemed alarmed, as visions of men – wet, muscular and naked – invaded my thoughts.

'They wouldn't actually swim here! We're a few kilometres from the base's township; there's a whole lot of wildlife between you and them. Let's take a look at the house.' Placing a hand on my back, she guided me away from the cliff. We walked to the house in silence, her face plastered with a game-show smile. Resting against the building was an aged and overturned eight-person dinghy. Davina tapped the hull. 'This here is a real piece of history. Dates back to the Second World War. My last visitor told me it was worth more than the land – bargain, hey?!'

I peered under the dingy. Its core was rusted, and only fragments of bench remained. A gold logo, faded, had been painted onto the stern: a three-headed water serpent, dazzling and ready to strike.

'Hydra,' Davina said.

I gasped at the coincidence: that was also the name of the Aegean island where my marriage had fallen apart.

'A gatekeeper to the Underworld,' she continued. 'It's the base's namesake: HMAS *Hydra*.'

Inside the shack Davina showed me two dusty bedrooms, a bathroom, and an open kitchen and living space with a deep stone fireplace that had its original rotisserie. The bathroom and kitchen had been redone in the 50s with avocado-green tiles, but the house was a knockdown that for some reason had been heritage listed.

Davina seemed to think this was a selling point. 'You couldn't tear the thing down, even if you wanted to,' she said, all smiles.

Utilities, she informed me, were separate from the base, and the postbox was back on the main road to save the postie trekking the three-kilometre drive.

'No one to disturb you,' she said.

We exited the house, and she walked me back to my car. 'Married? Kids?'

'A husband, Hayden, and we're trying.'

She looked at me approvingly. 'The base is selling the land off for pennies. They aren't even advertising it!' She handed me the Section 27 statement. 'I am obliged to tell you that, *technically*, it's not a land purchase as such but a hundred-year lease. Everything in this clearing is yours, or can be. Walk a few paces into surrounding scrub and that wire fence appears again.'

I scanned the perimeter, glimpsing some of the yellow trespass warnings. 'Can I remove the signs?'

'Probably not.'

Still looking at the signs, I warmed to the idea of being locked in this wild prison. There was comfort in their cage – perhaps I deserved to be locked away – and also feverishness, at thoughts of breaking free.

'Have I tempted you?' Davina said.

7

I t took two and a half weeks for the paperwork to settle and a further four days for me to claim the property as my own.

The first morning in my new shack I woke stiff on uneven floorboards. My yoga mat had done little to pad splinters that grew thorn-like during the night.

I'd arrived late afternoon the day before. Davina had been there to greet me and hand over the keys, her eyes darting from car to house and back again as if searching for someone. My husband? A veil of disappointment draped her face when she realised the key exchange was to include only me, myself and I.

As the sun dipped I went to bed, reading *Antiques Gazette* for an hour by candlelight before pulling the sleeping bag over my head to muffle any faceless night noises.

On yawning that first morning, I watched fog escape my mouth – without furniture, gas or electricity, the house was ghastly cold. The amenities would be turned on in the afternoon. Mobile phone reception was poor, 3G at best, and Davina had advised that I make calls from the main road – not that I had anyone to speak to. There was no internet, and I was reluctant to have it installed, knowing I would enjoy my self-imposed exile and a reprieve from online knick-knack trading. I had even stopped checking emails and turned off notifications on my phone. What was the point? I was only ever alerted to spam.

I slid on jeans and gumboots. My goal was to revive the house: a tunnel vision, I've since realised, preserving me like a pickle from noxious thoughts of unemployment. Every surface, windowsill, light fitting and doorknob was caked in dust and grime, and it's important to work with a clean canvas. As Lawrence would say, 'You can't discern truffles when they're buried in boar shit.' And while most of my possessions weren't worthy of Geoffrey Browne's attention, I wasn't accustomed to living in excrement.

To boil water for a black tea, I lit the fire with old matches that had been left on the stone mantel. Outside the air was crisp, damp. This was the first time I had seen the property so early in the day. The surrounding trees and shrubs were high and dense enough to shield me from the sun, which approached from inland, its light catching in the sandy soil, illuminating a golden hue. I steamed my face with the hot tea and wiped crust from my eyes. Morning dew covered spear grass and flax lily, three willie wagtails called to each other, and the verandah creaked underfoot. I was a postcard of Australiana, blowing proudly on my English breakfast.

I thought of my mother. Had she, surveying her new purchases, eased breath and unknotted stomach? By buying the property I'd sidelined my shadows: smashing china, unemployment, unspeakables. Had my mother done something similar? I had thought her never-ending cycle of dissatisfaction a quirk, an eccentricity common in those who inherit, but perhaps I was wrong. Had she too been running house to house in order to escape from something? If this were the case, her amnesty had been short-lived. How long before my own shadows emerged from the periphery?

A tour was in order. I needed to understand the property, the confines in which I was to live, and, more importantly, to disassociate the title's flaws from my own, so that even if the smashing china returned, I wouldn't abandon my new home in search of quieter sanctuary.

I walked to the eastern corner of the land, where cliff met scrub. Bush-bashing a few metres, I battled trees and glistening cobwebs, until I found HMAS *Hydra*'s wire fence and the boundary of my property. The wire was cold, slippery. I held on with one hand and walked the perimeter, only letting go when overgrown flora obscured my path, or when the scrub broke and the fence turned inland to make way for the dirt drive. Every thirty or so metres was another yellow sign forbidding trespassers, hidden among blackberry brambles. I wondered for whom these warnings were intended. Moving consciously, I listened to bark crunch underfoot and breathed deep the wetlands' salt-mineral air. My confidence grew with every step, the space now known, chartered. By the time I reached the opposite side of the cliff, the sun had illuminated the surrounding bush. Basking in my acquisition, I unbuckled my jeans and squatted above the ground, splashing my gumboots and the forbidden side of the fence line.

Back inside I opened all windows, releasing spirits and flooding my shack with light and air. Unlocking cupboards and drawers, I found three rusted nails, a brass doorknob, a mute whistle, and a man's lone Reebok sneaker. Other than these items the naval base had done well removing all effects. The house felt as though it had long been retired.

I began with the bedrooms – spraying, dusting and sweeping. The main bedroom had two large windows: one at the back of the house, overlooking the dirt drive, and the other at the side with views of a moonah that bent over as if frozen mid-dance. I made plans to hang a birdbath. The second bedroom was smaller with only one window, though it was otherwise identical with its moonah view, single hanging light bulb and cracked ivory walls. I washed away grime and polished fixtures. Then I unhooked the thin cream curtains and soaked them in the freshly scrubbed bath, twisting and pulling at their fabric. The soapy water soon turned brown so I rinsed and repeated, then hung them over the verandah railing to dry.

For breakfast and lunch I ate bread, jam and cheddar I'd brought from the city. For dinner, after the power and gas came on, I heated two-minute noodles and ate from the pot while standing over the sink. By midnight, with my jumper tied around my head as protection against dust mites, I'd cleaned my last ceiling lamp, killed five spiders, punctured my thumb and broken one kitchen-cabinet door. I showered (my run-off water resembling that from my curtains), crawled into my sleeping bag and slept like the dead.

The second morning I woke at dawn again, ensuring I'd be on time to meet the removalists at my old apartment. Earlier in the week I'd encountered a challenge: when typing my new address into Google Maps, I'd discovered that it simply didn't exist, the screen centring on a lake in the middle of the wetlands. My narrow drive was only to be found by zooming out and dragging the screen across, which reminded me that 1 Marsh Drive had until recently been an unnamed portion of classified land. It would have been near impossible to describe the driveway to city removalists; conversely, there was petrol money and tedious traffic to consider, but in any case I had to return the apartment key.

I found myself with eyes closed, holding tight the wall of the elevator as it soared fifteen floors. I knew my vertigo was really an unease generated by the remembrance that just as I'd boxed my valuables, so too had I stored my shadows. Cleaning the beach house had sublimated shame from certain realities, but here in the city I worried about being sprung by a jack-in-the-box.

It wasn't until I was back on the freeway, removalists and all my worldly possessions trailing me, that I began to relax. But I kept one eye fixed on my rear-vision mirror, just in case the truck slipped into oncoming traffic, and all that connected me to the past went up in flames. At the entrance to the peninsula, I pushed down on the accelerator. There was nothing left binding me to the city.

The two removalists worked fast and shared the load bearing in silence, one pushing, the other pulling. They were all brawn and buck, hard and undulating, bodies carved with testosterone. Occasionally one man would raise an object above his head, revealing the soft matted hair nestled in his underarm; I found it endearing as one would any small creature hiding in a cave. At one stage they jumped on the decaying verandah, voicing scepticism as to whether or not the wood would hold both them and my leather couch – a ramp was needed, a support beam – but as beautiful as the men were, I'd played games with removalists before. The key is to show no interest in their concerns, and when I merely turned my face to the water they took in the couch without another word.

This was a Geoffrey Browne trick; recalling it reminded me it was Monday and the staff would have their own vans to unload. Bertie had probably made his weekly trip to the city, informing all what a hopeless archivist I was. Would they be shocked at the depths of my desperation? Question how I'd got his contact details? Sue me for privacy infringement, fire Ian for failing to lock me out of the online portal? Would Ian have to fire himself? Maybe they'd say, 'Who is Anja?' And Fran would say, 'I think she was that girl with the dislike for Susie Cooper.' They would all nod in agreement, and I would be just another ghost who may or may not have trod their halls.

When the removalists had finished, I made them a cup of tea and they sat in silence on the verandah, either staring at their mugs or out at the ocean. Not knowing when I'd next have company, I attempted conversation. What items did they most enjoy transporting? Had they ever damaged something of great worth? But the gap separating us was wider than a few years in age. They gave one-word answers to open-ended questions, left their tea half drunk and were gone before lunch. Had they been warned to keep their distance? They worked for the removalist company Geoffrey Browne employed. Could news of my failings have reached one of our contractors? I wriggled my shoulders, shaking free the thought. It was no longer my problem.

Inside my kitchen and surrounded by boxes, I was confronted again with déjà vu. Another home, another new beginning. I was glad to have put little effort into unpacking the apartment. The boxes had been there to greet me on my return from Greece. Hayden had unburdened himself of me with little more than an email requesting a forwarding address. I was certain, though: this was it, no more houses. I was not my mother; I had walked the perimeter, made peace with the property's confines. And I could see the apartment as just a stepping stone, a transient space between my breakup, my firing and now, whatever 'now' was to be.

I took my time unpacking, relishing the reveal and placement of each object. Dusting or washing everything before it was put away. There were items I had forgotten owning, junk Hayden had bestowed me, and the knowledge that a few cherished chattels had been commandeered. The issue with objects, though, is that they tend to outlive flesh; they are concrete memories, evocations of people and places, some of which are long gone. I worked faster, aware of losing myself in sentimentality.

Then I pulled from a box the orange fondue pot and its seven long forks. There had once been eight.

Hayden and I had thrown a fondue party to celebrate his winning a case, or joining the Bar, or some other law-related activity. We were eight people for eight fondue forks. At the end of the party only seven forks remained. The lost fork hadn't been put in the rubbish, nor was it down the drain – I wrenched sink pipes apart in my search.

'There are two possible answers,' I told Hayden with spanner and rag in my hands, my arms covered in rubbish-bin grime. 'One: it was taken by one of our friends.'

'Our friends don't steal sticks.'

'*Forks* ... Two: it shifted planes.'

'Or three: you haven't found it yet. It's probably fallen through a crack!' Hayden had unfailing faith in random, rational cracks, his logic having the inverse effect of making me appear groundless and naive.

Staring then at the unwrapped fondue set, I realised I had to get rid of it; I'd never throw a fondue party without fear of losing another fork.

Falling down memory lane was unsettling, as was knowing I wasn't in control of what rose from the boxes. My belongings grew heavier when I lifted them towards the light, their weight grinding against my nerves. I began to resent dipping my hand into the unknown.

For the sake of self-preservation I observed each object clinically, dissecting it as if it were catalogued in the taxonomy discussed in my thesis. I opened a fresh box and pulled out a newspaper-wrapped drinking glass: vessel, water, water bearer, womb. Next was a silver serving tray: presentation, performance, exhibition. I delighted in the psychoanalytical play, the contrast between internal and external, hidden and exposed, the seemingly arbitrary plucking of items when Freud had attested that there is no such action as coincidence.

Then, to my horror, I took out the Danish salt-and-pepper shakers. This was a test; they were a wedding present from my father who, although invited, hadn't attended. I held them high and knocked them together like drumsticks counting in a band. Their meaning was threefold: universal denotations (balance and pairing, to enhance, to mask), initial personal connotations (heritage, lineage, affection), and secondary personal connotations (those I'd discovered a year after my wedding, at my mother's funeral).

My father had arrived late to the funeral; he'd snuck in during the ceremony and sat in the back row. It had been a decade since I'd last seen him. '*Hej*, Anja, it is me, Edmund,' he said, as if there was a chance I'd forgotten who he was.

I'd phoned his Danish mobile a week earlier – hoping the number hadn't changed – and left a message but had never heard back. The last thing I'd expected was for him to fly across the world for me, though there he was. He'd made an effort, and I felt like falling into his arms and never standing again.

We stood side by side outside the funeral home as mourners departed. It was fair to say nobody there knew who he was – or, if they'd been around back then, they were yet to reconcile the nineteen-year-old boy to the forty-seven-year-old man.

'I am compelled to assist with any arrangements,' he said.

I was on the verge of thanking him, of telling him I would be grateful for his help and the chance to spend time together. Perhaps losing one parent to the cosmos had opened room for the other. But when I turned to face him, it wasn't me he was looking at: it was a four-wheel drive parked across the road. There was a woman in it and two teenagers, their faces against the windows. Lina, Isabella and Max: his family – my family. They stared at me and I at them with the uncanny wonder and detestation one experiences when observing monkeys in a zoo.

Edmund saw me looking at them and was quick to keep talking. 'My father died. Two years ago. There was much paperwork, more than you can imagine.'

Apparently I'd lost a grandfather too. *This is my moment*, I thought, *to say something so honest and revealing it will bind us for life*. But nothing came to mind.

'As a youth,' Edmund continued, 'my father attended

boarding school. He always remarked on it teaching him resilience and self-discipline. It was the reason, he would say, that he made his bed every morning – without fail – and why he had the strength of character to become a judge.' Edmund chuckled and shook his head as if remembering a private joke. 'Perhaps if I had gone to boarding school like him, my youth would not have been such a disaster.' He was full-teeth grinning, a beautiful smile without a hint of gum. The merriment was jarring but seemed to fit him better than his mourning suit, which was a size too big. 'My parents could not believe how their nineteen-year-old son was spending his time in Australia. So they told everyone that I was volunteering, helping Aboriginal children – "in the sandbox", as they would say.' He looked at me, enthused, as though he'd asked a question and was awaiting a response.

I attempted an encouraging moan, which sounded like that of a crippled cat.

'I heard this lie often,' he said. 'They told it to all their friends. I was then praised, over and over – and, you know, living with praise one does not deserve takes a toll. So, we moved here, to help. Lina is a doctor and —'

'Australia?'

'Alice Springs, a year ago. It is important to help disadvantaged children. We build houses, organise football games; Lina gives free medical advice. Our lives now have purpose. Our own children too are thriving, growing into remarkable human beings with a true sense of social responsibility.'

'So, when you received an invite to my wedding you were in Australia, not Denmark?'

'My mother forwarded the invite. We had just arrived and

needed to settle in. No point to uprooting the children for a weekend.'

I nodded. 'Aha, aha. But your present, the salt-and-pepper shakers, they're Danish?'

'Yes, I suppose they are. Like me.' He laughed. 'My mother posted them. Postage abroad is quite expensive, is it not?'

Holding the shakers then, I knew the secondary personal connotation: don't be fooled by phallic substitutes.

I was suddenly starving and grateful for my newly installed fridge. There are only good memories inside a fridge, although on opening the door I realised memories there may be, but food there was not. I again boiled water for two-minute noodles and ate from a bowl at my four-person dining table. The sky was black, rain drummed upon the roof, and a moth knocked endlessly against a lamp. The noodles tasted like plastic, and the three empty chairs were louder than any guest who had sat in them. I realised, between tasteless mouthfuls, that with no food delivery in the area and few restaurants, I'd have to be more self-reliant. Even if there had been people able to cook my every meal, I could no longer have denied the fact that money was fast running out. The land purchase had dropped my decade-long fiscal buffer to a mere few months. What game was I playing at, hunger Russian roulette?

How despicable had I become? I pictured the newspaper article:

Privileged Woman Starves to Death
After Overcapitalising

I rose from the table and stood at the kitchen sink, scrubbing clean my fork, bowl and mind.

On the third day I set my attention to a kitchen garden. The night's rain had passed, so I flipped the wartime dinghy over and dragged it to the centre of the clearing. It was heavier than I'd expected. Hydra's furious six eyes set upon me as I dared to disturb her slumber. To vex her further, I kicked away at her rotten benches, leaving just the shell of her hull, then drilled holes through her base for drainage. She'd be repurposed, whether she liked it or not. Her paint markings had long ago washed away so that her only connection to her past life was the ferocious gold logo perched at the stern inside her hull.

At the store (and leaving me with my last few thousand dollars), I bought a shovel, trowel, pitchfork, gloves, shears, a variety of ceramic stakes, a marker to write on the stakes, pesticide and a watering-can (there was no sprinkler system on the property), and coriander, basil, cos lettuce, spinach, gold potatoes, beetroot, tomatoes (pink cherry and green zebra), and chilli (cayenne and ghost). Expensive, but I was certain to save in the long run. Quite pleased with my purchase, I made future plans: an outdoor pizza oven, chickens, and perhaps a goat for company. The opportunities were endless.

I also ordered a trailer of earth, fertiliser, and blood and bone to be delivered that morning. But it arrived late afternoon; my directions had been misunderstood, and the nurseryman had found himself kilometres away, trying to deliver to a confused sailor at the naval base. He finally found his way to me and asked if I would like the dirt heaped into the dinghy. I thanked him but insisted on doing it – I felt compelled to prove myself to Hydra. He shrugged, unlatched the tray door and tilted the trailer, creating a mound of dirt next to the dinghy.

When he left, I got to work shovelling dirt into the boat and patting it with the back of the spade. I was careful not to pile soil higher than her logo, leaving the fierce writhing heads exposed – an ode to the boat's origins. Don't mask the past: another lesson learned at Geoffrey Browne.

I'd never gardened before in my life, and my orifices weren't used to an onslaught of dirt. My hands blistered and my back spasmed. I rubbed my eyes and blew my nose on my hand. Black snot covered my palm. I wiped it on my pants and tried to breathe through my mouth as tears ran down my cheeks. With each spade full of soil, Hydra kept watch, gatekeeper to my beachfront underworld. If I were able to grow my own food, I'd never have to leave. Then she really would be keeping me here, guarding against my exit.

By the time I'd planted all the seeds and saplings and marked their locations with stakes, it was nearing sunset. I looked around for something else to do. My body ached and my head was foggy. I'd been working for days with little rest. I finally had to concede; I was scared to stop – in a moment of idleness, china might smash upon the floor. But there was no fight left in me. *Let it be*, I thought as I opened a bottle of red.

I headed outside with my glass and bottle to where two Adirondack chairs had been placed unprompted near the cliff's edge by the removalists, as if they'd tuned in to Davina's summer-night fantasy. A cool breeze came from across the sea, and I wrapped my woollen jumper tighter around my body. I'd barely paid attention to the water since I'd arrived. Did I dare to take a dip? Would others know of my trespass? Waves lapped against rocks in a continuous beat, and the sun began to bow behind the ocean. I poured another glass. *Breathe.*

In the distance and rounding the corner of my view were the remains of an abandoned cargo ship that had run aground in the 80s. The hollowed body, stripped of any equipment, tilted sideways, threatening to topple into the waves but forever correcting itself. It was a battleground, or so the nurseryman had told me, between local preservationists and council capitalists. Either way, all it contained were fish and barnacles, and deep-sea diving was all its haunting shell was good for.

I stayed seated long after the sun had set and I had lost sight of the vessel. With the bottle emptied I stood, a little wobbly, and turned to face the house. It was darker than I'd expected. The kitchen light was on, illuminating the verandah, but the property was otherwise black – not even Hydra's dinghy was visible. I could no longer discern what was open space and what was perimeter; it was as if the surrounding bush had crept in.

I set off into the dark for the house. Metres from the verandah, I smelt it – foul, pungent. I quickened my pace, not knowing from which direction the smell came.

And then I froze. Feet away, illuminated on the doorstep: faeces.

The turds were large, dark, wet. Someone had been squat, staring at the back of my head while loosening their bowels.

I gripped the wine bottle. My eyes darted, but there was nothing to see, nothing that could be seen. I dashed towards the house, leaping over the excrement and throwing myself at the front door, which, of course, was unlocked!

I crept into the kitchen, my back against the wall, and took a knife from the block then slunk back towards the front door, locking it. I searched under beds, cupboards, behind curtains, in empty boxes, the bath, behind all doors. The shit's stench had infected every corner of the house.

After a fretful half-hour, I was content that I was alone. I could call someone, but whom? Beth, who lived two hours away? Hayden, who wanted nothing to do with me? Fran, just to hear her cackle? I turned my attention to the darkness outside. All my curtains were open. The bastard had probably been watching me the entire time. I threw each curtain shut and crawled into bed with my knife.

At first light on the fourth day, I put on dishwashing gloves, picked up the hardened shit and tossed it into the bush. The property was now mine.

[ITEM 4]
10:00, 14 September 1985.
Interview — Mango Hall: Lieutenant Brendan
Quartermain & Petty Officer Matthew Gibbs.

BQ: When I asked to speak with the officers
involved, I didn't expect to see you here. You
didn't mention anything to me yesterday.

MG: No, Sir. I was instructed only to show you
to your quarters. I didn't think it necessary to
divulge unofficially, before the interview.

How long have you been stationed at HMAS ▇▇▇▇*,*
Officer Gibbs?

Eighteen months, Sir. I'm originally from
Rockhampton. Started my naval career seven years
ago, up north in Cairns, travelled down the
eastern board ever since. This is my last stop on
the mainland, then it's Hobart, and then … who
knows? Antarctica, at the Casey Station, I guess?

Haven't spent too much time deployed, then?

No, Sir. Don't thrive in confined spaces … Before
I signed up I had thought of the ocean as freedom,
the big vast open. It's embarrassing to confess
but turns out my mind bucks at endless sinkable
space, can't metabolise it. Take me out to sea
and it's like sticking me in a coffin — trapped,
constricted, can't breathe — and no one's keen to
work with a drowning man.

What field do you specialise in?

Ordnance training, small arms. I train the new recruits. Preliminary stuff as well: ropes, uniform maintenance. But guns are my speciality. I'm head officer in charge of the shooting range. If you like, we can head there during your stay — you can fire a few rounds.

Thank you. I'll keep that in mind. The night of your involvement, can you talk me through the events that led to your discovery?

It was Recruit Week, formal dinner in the dining hall, with all the officers and new recruits. We'd just finished dessert — chocolate mousse — and Commander Wilson was addressing the room as he does every Wednesday; he speaks of the achievements and challenges of the past week and any other order of business that needs discussing. That night he mentioned that recruits would soon be issued with identification cards, and that's when I realised I'd left my security pass on my desk at the shooting range. It's a violation to not have your pass on you, so I waited for dinner to finish and then jumped in my jeep and headed towards the wetlands.

Gate D is the closest wetlands entrance to my range and has security stationed there to check who goes in and out. It's restricted to officers and accompanied recruits. As you know, it's a huge nature reserve, but scattered inside there's a safety school, my shooting complex, a couple of research labs and your cottage, so we like to know who's coming in and out of the area. Anyway, I was lucky. That night Officer Casper was rostered on at the security checkpoint and he knows me well, just ushered me in. Good thing, as he'd be forced to write me up if he had realised I couldn't produce a pass.

To the shooting range, it's a fifteen-minute drive down a dirt road. I had my high beams on. You have to be careful of 'roos, you know, 'cause there aren't any street lamps. We like to keep the animals in as natural an environment as possible — especially that long-toothed bandicoot, ugly bastard. Nocturnal. Have you heard of it? … Anyway, we fire the crap out of our guns during the day but don't disturb the wildlife at night. Mind if I smoke? [sound of match striking and cigarette lighting]

So, I arrived at the shooting range and pulled into the drive next to my office. When I turned off the car, the only things lighting my path were the moon and the low-watt lamp hanging above the office door. [long pause]

Go on.

I put my key in the door and, as I went to turn it, the hair on my arms stood on end. I was suddenly scared shitless. I'm not going to pretend I can explain it — it's not a sensation I've felt before — but I just knew … I was being watched.

I spun around. There was a figure 200 metres away, crawling between targets at the end of the range. Down low, like they were in the trenches. The moonlight barely skimmed them, but I know what I saw.

And what details did you see? Height, build?

It was hard to tell — like I said, it was dark
— but instinct told me it was female. The way
her backside held in the air

there was a slight curve in the spine and a rounding at the hip

Most women have a dip in their lower back. Raises
their arses in the air when they're doing planks.
Men don't have that. Our backs are straight —
rigid. Don't cave easy. You know what I mean? I
also think she was naked or perhaps in leggings,
something close to the skin. No bulging clothes
or heavy boots, no webbing belt or backpack. The
lines of her body were sleek.

And what did you think she was doing?

I thought this was some kind of prank, because no
one should have been down there. As I said, it was
Recruit Week, which meant we had to be vigilant.
Recruits often fool around in their first week
— push the boundaries with stuff like streaking
and out-of-bounds behaviour. We knock it out of
them pretty quick: few extra sit-ups, a twenty-
kilometre run usually shakes them into shape.

What did you do next?

I yelled out, 'The fuck you doing?' And she froze.
I took a step forward and she threw herself behind
a target. I finished unlocking the office door and
switched on the main light. The spotlight flooded
the range and I ran the 200 metres down towards
the targets. But when I got there she was gone. No

sign of her. Must have fled the second it took me to turn the key in the door. But then I looked down.

There was something shiny in the grass. It was a medal, a fucking historic medal! And this pissed me right off as doing a naked dash is one thing but breaking into the archives and stealing war memorabilia is another. Someone like that has no respect, can't be taught and has no place in the Royal Australian Navy.

Who did you first report the breach to?

Everyone. I was livid. I sped back to camp, hit the sirens and the lamps, and woke up all the recruits, dragged them from their dorms into the dining hall, made them sit there till someone spoke up — owned up — no bathroom breaks, nothing.

Did anyone come forward?

No, and no one was missing. I counted the women twice. Then a couple of hours later Commander Wilson put an end to it. Informed me that there was no sign of a break-in at the archives, or any other breach, so I had to let them go.

It took me a while to settle down that night, but I finally fell asleep. It wasn't until the morning that I could think straight, and I realised then that there was no way a recruit could have beaten me back to their dorm. They'd been on foot, and there hadn't been any other cars in the wetlands that night, which meant I was looking in the wrong place. She was someone who knew the area, someone of higher rank. That's why we kept quiet about the second incident. We didn't want to alarm the newbies nor lose face to the Poms who were about to pay us a visit.

Where's the medal now?

I gave it back to the archivist. These things need to be treasured, remembered: sacrifice, boundaries, territory.

You realise I'm not here to investigate trespassing and a medal that may or may not have been stolen?

Sure, but I reckon the two events are linked. That's why I asked to be the first to speak with you, so you can understand the scenario, see the whole picture.

What makes you think the events are linked?

[sound of match striking and cigarette lighting] I run the shooting range — that's my territory — and Petty Officer Robbins, he runs the safety school, that's his domain. I think I caught someone in the act of doing something on my turf, but then I busted them before they had a chance to pull it off, so they had to go to Plan B, which was Officer Robbins.

You think this was personal?

Like I said, I came here from Rockhampton. Moved my way down the coast. Officer Robbins, he's also from Rockhampton. We trained, graduated and started working together in Cairns. I know him pretty well — decent guy, good underwater, keeps his cool. A real asset to any crew. Quiet, though, even more so these days than before. Prefers his own company. Hell! He'll see you walking towards him and do a 180 just to be by himself. Can't take it personal. Long story short, he was deployed and I was transferred after allegations against us were made.

What kind of allegations?

The kind where it's your word against another's and that other is a whole lot prettier than you. Anyway, it was a long time ago. I was re-stationed, kept my head down, lost contact with him — until, that is, we found ourselves here together. Then two months ago, posters started appearing around base.

Posters?

On poles, communication boards, behind flywire, under windscreen-wipers. Insinuating posters. Accusatory. The kind that suggest a whole lot without actually saying anything, pinpointing anyone. Just a bunch of theatrical language: pillage, ravage, plunder, desecrate. Whoever the author is, they're living on hot air, don't know all the facts. It's a defamation case — we could sue. That's what I told Robbins.

So these posters and incidents were directed at the two of you?

You think it's a coincidence?

A note to the reader: Items 5 & 6 of the report have been omitted.

8

If Beth were a Wegner chair she would be a PP250 Valet –
practical to a fault. That's why I didn't tell her about the
porch poo. She would have taken action: dragged me to the
hardware store, installed security traps, phoned the police. She
would have been right to: it was an explicit threat, an invasion
of privacy, a concrete message to cease and desist. It was also
intimate, a communication meant only for me, my eyes, my
nostrils. The gesture had been nagging at me for a fortnight,
and I found myself checking under my shoes, even when
walking inside the house, as if a wet stinky pile could emerge
like magic from the floorboards.

There was also a sense of guilt. Perhaps I deserved the
present on my doorstep. Had I conjured it with my rebellious
thoughts of diving headfirst into the cold, dark, out-of-bounds
ocean? Would sailors capture me? Shoot me on sight? Could I,
a lone woman treading water, be such a threat that they'd raise
their guns? Loosen their bowels?

Beth arrived midafternoon while I was tending the
vegetable patch. To assist visitor navigation, I'd painted red the
small boulder used to prop open my farm gate. Her Range
Rover pulled into the clearing, and she emerged from the car

with an armful of orange roses and an overnight bag. 'A lot of trespass signs – it's very tempting!' she yelled across the clearing, causing branched birds to take flight.

Beth was raised never to say anything insincere and to hold her tongue at negativity. In theory, someone who expresses only honesty and positivity should be charming and agreeable; instead she'd become proficient in conversational poker, often skirting issues and complimenting that which should have been criticised. And the more stretched the compliment, the louder her voice, as if by yelling she could hide her true thoughts.

I led her inside the cottage and arranged the roses in a Bitossi vase while she stood by the cast-iron fireplace, warming the backs of her legs. 'It's heritage listed, isn't it?' she said, looking up at rotting wooden beams. 'You could probably get that overturned.'

I handed her a glass of the Shiraz she'd brought.

'Good drop, this one,' she said. 'Got it from the cellar.' Whenever Beth said she'd 'got it from the cellar', she meant she'd ridden a glass elevator to a subterranean sandstone storage facility that was as big as a hockey pitch.

She cupped the glass in her hands and bit her lip. I could tell she wanted to ask me what I was doing. Why had I blown my inheritance on an isolated and restricted property? Why hadn't I waited for another job in the city, stayed with Hayden, tried for kids?

Instead she said, 'I'm excited about tonight!' She was speaking of the restaurant she'd chosen, which featured in all the culinary mags and culture-vulture websites. She was also keen to point out the supposed fuckability of the head chef.

I smiled, unable to remember the last time I'd dined at a hatted restaurant.

'It will do you good to get out and meet some people here,' she said. 'Like-minded, enterprising people.'

Beth was what my mother had referred to as 'socially ambitious'. She was also shrewd. At graduation, she had confessed to me a 'take-over plan' for the vineyard that she'd been enacting since her early teenage years: on realising daughters rarely inherit family farms, she'd begun a campaign to convince her older brother that viticulture was a dying industry; he was meant for grander things, for soul-searching work. That's why he ended up living in a commune in Byron. She laughed about it later. 'I was right after all,' she often said. 'He was never cut out for the industry – roots weren't strong, uplifted too easily.'

I plated brie and quince paste, and took a seat at the plastic table and chairs on the verandah.

'Absolutely not,' Beth said. 'What's the point of having such a view if you don't enjoy it?' She ran ahead of me towards the cliff's edge and threw herself down into one of the wooden chairs.

I hadn't sat there since being 'gifted'. I'd often walked to the edge, admiring the water, but never sat down and relaxed. Never turned my back too long to the house.

'What's wrong?' Beth said, when she caught me surveying the shrubs. 'Keeping watch for sailors?'

I laughed to hide my guilt and sat next to her, letting out a deep breath for what felt like the first time in two weeks. With Beth keeping watch, my anxieties drifted on the wind out to sea. I closed my eyes. I hadn't heard china smash in weeks –

that was auspicious – and Hydra would soon be fruiting. Petite stalks had sprung, and the chilli saplings had grown a good few inches.

Beth leant over and rubbed my hand. 'You're going to be fine. You'll get another job, perhaps start your own dealership. You'll make friends here, a partner. That heritage listing will be overturned. It's all going to be fucking fabulous.'

I opened my eyes. 'I first need to finish the vegetable patch.'

She turned to look at the dirt mound I'd stuck a shovel into. 'Well,' she eventually said, 'you may need to get digging then.'

We ordered a taxi just after dark. The driver was late, and Beth grew agitated. Despite being a country girl, she shrank in silence and isolation, and when the sun bowed on my property there was nothing but possums and stars. She'd grown up with a sibling to torment, parents fawning over her, and a barn full of labourers who were often at the dining table, and I could tell she was unnerved by this seaside solitude.

She was marching around the house as she searched for a phone signal when I realised she wasn't alone at all – she was with me! Something had grown between us that the dark brought to light. She hadn't always been anxious in my presence, keen to fill conversation lulls with an endless sequence of facts sourced from Google.

But perhaps I was overthinking the matter. When we were at school she'd always gravitated to the loudest table, the most populated square. It was I who needed time alone, often enjoying a private smoke while lying in long grass at the centre of the old oval. I was used to the quiet. It had always just been Mum and me, and then it had been Hayden and me, and now ...

Beth was attempting fact checks on plankton when headlights flooded the drive and shone into the house. 'Finally!' she said, grabbing her handbag. 'I hate being late.'

The taxi driver rolled down his window. 'This isn't what I was expecting. We still on base?'

'It's private land now,' Beth said, getting in.

We buckled up in the back seat, but the driver just sat staring towards the ocean, or the house, or my veggie patch. 'You live here together?' he said.

'Yes,' we said in unison.

'Bet the boys on base love that!'

Beth rolled her eyes and handed the driver her phone with the restaurant's address.

'Let me guess, ladies, uphill?'

'How observant,' she said.

The driver did a U-turn and drove back up the dirt path. 'Well, it was either uphill to the wineries or downhill to the docks, and you two aren't dressed for that.'

When we reached the farm gate I saw he'd left it open and had every intention of driving off with it still ajar, as if the land were public property.

'Pull over,' I said and jumped out to shut the gate. I realised then that I hadn't left the property since I'd stocked up at the local store a week ago.

I couldn't decide if it was a bad thing or a good thing or a nothing that perhaps I was becoming a hermit. I'd spent my days reading, cleaning and gardening, not once thinking about the outside world. Were there hours I couldn't account for? Days? If Beth hadn't arrived to shake me from my dreamlike solitude, how long would it have been before I re-emerged in public, and would that person have been entirely different from the one I was now?

I didn't like to acknowledge it to myself, but I felt solace in keeping watch over the property, as if my presence might drive off intruders. Perhaps I was scared to leave.

We drove down the empty stretch of road, and I counted the yellow signs as I'd done over a month ago. Had Bertie found his archivist?

'Busy night?' I said to the driver, trying to forget those nimble fingers.

'Slow, now,' he said, 'but it'll pick up around ten, when the sailors want to head downhill. I'll call it quits around 2 a.m., after I've delivered food to the girls at Sirens House – they're famished by that time.'

Beth leant forward into the front seat. 'A brothel?'

'Same order every time: ten cheeseburgers, ten large fries and ten Cokes. Occasionally, once a month, one of them orders a chocolate sundae. I like to think it's a celebration sundae, cause one of 'em has had their own little orgasm.'

'Here's hoping!' Beth said, her eyes gleaming as they often did when friends made faux pas or strangers misjudged social cues.

I couldn't feel her titillation. The story was wretched: women sustained on fast food and a driver who'd hitched his moral compass to a self-anointed 'celebration' sundae. And by hearing about the women's hour off, I felt as if I'd infringed upon their private time. Or maybe my unease was because I'd been only a laugh away from joining them.

'If I haven't another customer,' the driver continued, 'I'll buy my own burger and eat with the girls. I like watching them get stuck into their junk food. It's quite the scene, you know, them in their lingerie and me in my driving suit. All of us sitting around and enjoying some deep-fry. They're messy eaters. Get more fat on their faces than they do their backsides – must be all the exercise.'

'Appetising,' Beth said with blunt force.

'They're polite, you know, well mannered. Great listeners too. If I've problems, they're willing to hear me out. Take an actual interest in me, unlike many passengers.'

It was a provocation: not just the dig at snobby passengers, but the whole story.

Beth took the bait. 'Sounds like you're a regular,' she said, looking at her phone – she only enjoyed the tease, never the reveal.

'Oh, I don't use their services if that's what you mean. Don't think the misses would be too pleased about that. I just deliver food and let the sailors have all the fun. It's costly, you know.' He tapped the metre. 'Fifty dollars for a hand job, eighty dollars for a blow job – that's with a condom; they won't blow you without one, new rule. I did the calcs. It's six dollars twenty for a burger, so one gobby can get you 12.9 burgers. And one wristy can get you 16.66 medium fries at three dollars a pack. This is all prior to rounding, of course. No such thing as a fraction of a burger or half a servicing – unless you don't cum.'

I thought it through; he was right. Beth rolled down her window and peered out, signalling an end to the conversation.

As we pushed uphill and away from the beach, it didn't take long for the landscape to morph from dried, twisted tree trunks to lush, mossy greens; even the moonahs grew skyward when protected from the offshore breeze. Houses stood among manicured gardens and stone walls, and I wondered which of them my mother would have fallen for.

The further inland we drove, the more Beth's posture eased. When the driver paused at an intersection, she placed her head out the window and breathed in the damp forest air, then turned to me and smiled. I was struck – this was the most relaxed I'd seen her in years. Locked in a car but not alone, she could empty her mind and exist peacefully for a brief moment between expressing her concern for me and attempting to charm clients at the upmarket restaurant.

Her serenity was short-lived. When the 'Goostronomic' sign appeared over the rise, her back straightened and she shook out her hair. We pulled into a gravel carpark illuminated by wooden box lamps. The fare came to thirty dollars, and Beth handed over her Visa without a word.

'Enjoy your dinner, ladies,' the driver said with an unnerving intimation.

'Impotent,' Beth said as the car drove off.

From a distance the restaurant appeared to be carved into a hill. On closer inspection, it was apparent that the lawn roof had been added and that the slight curve of the hill wasn't a natural formation but rather a structure that ascended from the ground like a rolling knoll. Atop the roof was a beehive, vegetable garden and two rows of vines.

'A Friedensreich Hundertwasser inspiration,' said a male voice from behind us. The attempted Germanic accent was brutish and alarming.

Beth and I spun around. The man was wearing a white chef's uniform and holding a fresh bunch of rosemary.

Beth kissed his cheeks before introducing us: me as her 'oldest and dearest friend', and him as 'Noah Burns, head chef of the groundbreaking Goostronomic'. He had a weak chin and was not as fuckable as she had led me to believe.

'The great man was a Viennese architect,' Noah continued, as if uninterrupted, spitting out his 'w's as 'v's. 'Hundertwasser believed we should live sustainably, eat locally. He felt that if one *must* live indoors, then the roof should be green to irrigate run-off rainwater. Remarkably advanced for a man born in 1928, don't you think? He also said all straight lines are *torture*, hence there isn't a straight line in the entire building. Well, except for the kitchen, of course.'

'Fascinating,' Beth cooed.

'And having our kitchen garden elevated also keeps rabbits out. They're at plague levels on the peninsula.'

I thought of Hydra's vegetable patch. 'I haven't seen one rabbit since I moved here.'

'Mustn't be growing anything they fancy,' Noah said, and Beth laughed.

I was determined to pinpoint a straight line when two preened black sheep roamed onto a nearby petanque sandpit.

'Chops and Dice,' Noah said. 'We won't eat them.' He excused himself and went behind the restaurant.

Beth linked my arm in hers, and we walked towards the entrance. I liked feeling her so close; there was reassurance in her woollen jumper caressing my own. Truth was, though, I could cuddle her dead but she would never again crack open for me. Somewhere in our mid-twenties she had sealed up, cemented that gap of vulnerability only I'd once seen. Was Miles ever privy to it? Knowing too much about a person is a ticking threat of shame and embarrassment that leaves you and them exposed. I knew her darkest secrets: she'd plagiarised half her schoolwork, she secretly judged fat people, and at fifteen she'd slept with an anonymous trucker in a highway motel. Was Beth the woman held hostage by my knowledge of Beth the girl? Of course, she knew my twisted shames as well: those I'm unwilling to speak aloud, even today. Perhaps that was the real reason I'd lied to her about the faeces – I too was sealed and silent. But there, at the entrance to that hobbit hut, I leant in closer to her, enjoying those few remaining seconds in which I, at least, could pretend we were riddled with chasms.

The menu – titled 'Spring' – featured artichokes, rocket, mint and peas with poussin and lamb as accent meats. Did Chops and Dice know their chic black wool had saved their hides? We had the choice between the degustation – eight courses – and the à la carte, which comprised three options per entrée, main and dessert. I wasn't too hungry and Beth rarely ate, but as she wasn't yet pregnant and I wasn't paying, we settled on the degustation with paired wines. Dishes were languidly timed, meaning I was drunk by the third course.

After the fourth, I began to take issue with the décor. The chef was right: walls, ceiling, windows, tables, chairs, doors, plates and art were all curved. I turned my head up and down, back and forth. 'Aha!' I said to Beth, pointing at the cash register. 'Angled. Straight.'

She reminded me that Goostronomic was a client.

Throughout the meal, our waiter was never far away and spoke to Beth with the manner of a long-lost friend, once even rolling his eyes at another table for her benefit. He laid each plate with exaggerated care, as if he were a jeweller presenting a box of diamonds. Between the sixth and seventh courses, with a wink, he produced a dish not on the menu. 'Contraband from Chef,' he whispered. 'Wild rabbit tortellini. Shot this morning and uninspected, so we can't charge for it.' Was Noah taunting me with his abundance of bunnies?

The waiter then invited us to join the festivities after service – it was the sommelier's birthday.

'This is why I love hospitality,' Beth said. 'Everyone knows how to have a fucking good time!'

We didn't discuss Hayden that night, or my lack of a job or direction. Not that I wanted to. Food, drink and décor provided much-desired distractions. The only evidence Beth felt concerned for me was that she asked if I was sure I wanted to stay for the party.

'Of course,' I said. 'You're the one who insisted I make friends.'

It was past midnight when the last diner had driven from the carpark. As their tail-lights disappeared into the bush, the waitstaff laid claim to the music, and the chefs brought from the kitchen large bowls of pasta, salads and Cornish pasties left over from the lunch service. We pushed together a row of tables with Noah taking the head, and Beth and I, as guests, at the opposite end.

Passing around a joint, I learned most staff lived locally, renting houses together in nearby towns. Noah was the only one who lived on the property; as part of his contract, he took up residence in the worker's cottage Thursdays through Sundays and spent the remainder of the week with his wife and daughter in the city.

After our plates were cleared, two chefs returned from the kitchen with a tarte Tatin spotted with flaming candles. We broke into 'Happy Birthday' and looped on to each other's waists. In single file we danced between tables, into the kitchen and up a spiral staircase to the rooftop garden, the tarte Tatin – giddy and ablaze – leading the way.

I was stirred by the staff's camaraderie. Would Fran have ever baked me a cake? *Happy birthday, Anja!* she would have sung. *Do you taste the love and hemlock?* I imagined the Geoffrey Browne staff gathering around with Lawrence instructing everyone to embrace and dance. *Who's Anja?* one colleague carolled. Another, *The one who dismissed collectibles.* Then they all chimed in, *Yes, yes, we showed her.*

I held Noah's waist as we climbed the stairs. Looking behind I could see Beth further down the conga line. She was staring up at me the way she had when we were at school and she'd caught me rolling my kilt twice to shorten it, not once. You were only to roll your kilt once.

9

The next morning, the sous-chef offered to drive us home, although it was out of his way. I got the impression this was less of an inconvenience than it would be to have us loitering as staff cleaned up after the night's festivities and prepared for the lunch service.

We broke through mossy forest and once more drove the deserted Hill Pass. The sun was rising over the paddocks, and the ground was wet with dew. I lay stretched across the back seat, my head too heavy for me to count any yellow signs. Beth was faring much better and sat up front with the sous-chef, who was speaking of harvests, soils, seasons – things I, at that moment, had no interest in. Then she was joking with him, guessing at the 'Summer' menu and suggesting he incorporate her Chardonnay.

When we arrived at the farm gate, I moved to sit up, but Beth was too fast and jumped out, ushering us through. It was a relief to be home. We drove down my driveway in silence, listening to the ocean grow louder. The car stopped at the clearing, and Beth and I got out.

'Don't like their chances,' the chef said, pointing at Hydra's boat. 'Salt air is corrosive. They'll struggle this close to the sea without a windbreak.'

He waved goodbye and drove off. I knelt to inspect my vegetable patch, taking the budding tomato leaves between my fingers.

'Well, I'll be off,' Beth said, throwing her overnight bag into her car.

'We could get breakfast?'

'And here I thought you already ate.'

'When?'

'Afterwards. I thought Noah would have cooked you a big, greasy gourmet burger.'

I stood. '*You* were the only one working last night.'

She slammed her car door and came towards me. 'I'm not going to apologise for networking – that's what sells bottles. Some of us still have to work. And anyway, *you're* also in sales, no matter how much you parade it as History. Or, at least, you were bef—'

'You weren't selling bottles, you were selling me: "Get to know locals! Make friends, upwardly mobile people!"' I hated the childish twang in my mock-Beth voice, but couldn't stop. '"The head chef is *so* fuckable. A *real* fuckfeast." Well, I'm telling you now, *Beth*, he wasn't that fuckworthy!'

Beth shook her head and groaned.

'Is *that* what this is about?' I said. 'You have a thing for Noah?' I let disgust hang on my face.

She was quiet for longer than I imagined. 'Yeah, maybe, why not, if I were single,' she said, losing some anger. 'But, Anja, grow up – that's not the point. I supply his wines not his women.'

I rolled my eyes, another childish act, revealing I was lost for comebacks.

'So, what's the plan?' She opened her arms wide. 'You're just going to live out here like a hermit? Survive on your inheritance, toil in your shitty boat?'

The dig at Hydra stung, and I didn't dare tell her that the money was gone, gobbled up by the infertile land we stood on. I wondered too at her boundaries. Why were my excesses more depraved than hers? Where once I was a confidante, an accomplice, I'd become more akin to her house plant: a cornered thing tended and watered occasionally. Actually, I was worse than a plant. She looked at me with overt revulsion, and it wasn't the feigned look of moral shock. The realisation we had grown apart was annihilating. Growing apart from me also meant growing apart from herself – best to let me be the whore.

I remembered waking with her on many mornings of our late teens and early twenties: sunlight cascading onto her face, black kohl still circling her eyes and staining my pillow, sheets always down past her stomach, exposing her breasts, while I slept with blankets up to my chin and a washed face no matter what time I retired. Legs and arms would be entwined, and we would lie together recapping the night's events, neither of us wanting to rise despite dying of thirst.

There was nothing left to say. She got into her car and, curiously, belted the empty passenger seat, as if driving away with fifteen years of friendship strapped next to her. I didn't move until the car was out of sight, and perhaps I even waited a few minutes longer. Finally, I turned, made toast and went to bed.

'Ptu, ptu, ptu.'
'They are spitting, at the Evil Eye.'

I woke with a fright in the late afternoon. Hydra! I'd forgotten to assess her salt damage. The sun was approaching the ocean as I ran from the house and bent to inspect her leaves. That sous-chef had been right: my grounded dinghy had sunk. Her budding leaves were yellow, stripped of their natural fibres and part way to hell. I hadn't seen it before; I hadn't wanted to. My kitchen garden investment, a waste of fucking time. I'd sunk hundreds on posts, soil, seeds and equipment. My stomach churned. My mother's last funds, blown on an idea, a conception, a miscarriage.

I calculated there was less than a thousand dollars left in the bank. I couldn't even pay council rates. I had to take action, to heed Beth's advice and grow up. I'd return to the world and online trading. First step: setting up the internet. I grabbed my phone and marched to the end of my drive to ring the service provider.

After twenty toe-tapping minutes, the call centre operator told me the NBN was years away. The area was working at maximum capacity, there were only so many fixed lines, the station's infrastructure was inadequate, there was a waitlist. Someone had to relinquish their connection before I could install mine.

'Someone has to die, you mean?'

'No,' she said, then repeated, 'someone has to give up their line.'

She'd been coached, but I was having none of it. 'And under what circumstances would someone give up their line?'

'Change of lifestyle.'

'Change of lifestyle, as in, death?'

'As in, they want to change the way in which they are living.'

'Would moving house be considered a change of lifestyle?'

'No, the line would remain with the house and be used by the new owners.'

'So, if one is not moving house yet one is giving up their line, would it be a stretch of the imagination to consider that any discontinued line had, in fact, been terminated along with other utilities by the dead person's relatives?'

'That would not constitute a change of lifestyle.'

'Because?'

'Because lifestyles are for the living.'

I kicked my farm gate and took a deep breath before agreeing to my placement on their waitlist.

Walking back down the lonely drive I listened as birds sang the day's final song. How many other animals – other lives – were in arm's reach, hidden by this dense scrub? My hangover had returned, brain pounding against skull shell. Beth would be home by now.

At the clearing I slumped next to the dinghy, peering into Hydra's damning eyes. She'd had purpose: sailing alongside destroyers in the 40s, transporting their precious loads to shore. What cargo had she held? And what would she have said if her mouth hadn't been full of fertiliser? I closed my eyes and wrapped my arms around her bow.

When I opened them again, a naval ship was sailing into view. It was the first one I'd seen since being there. Its cold, long body slid silently by my cliff's edge. A sailor on the deck caught sight of me. He held on to the ship's railing as he lifted his binoculars up and down. He beckoned to his fellow mariners, and three more of them came on deck, each with binoculars pointed at me. They were laughing and waving.

Was it one of these men who gifted me their shit? Was I nothing but a joke, a plaything for territorial sailors? A woman living alone on beachfront property – *Let's scare the knickers off her!* This was about ownership, proprietorship, possession.

I had once convinced my mother to remodel a kitchen – the only renovation she ever undertook. Builders filed in and set up their smoko station in the laundry, covering its benches with coffee-mug stains, cigarette ash and dog-eared porno mags. They browsed the porn during morning breaks, rubbing out a load before knock off. Each time my mother did the laundry, folded the clothes, she had to brush aside a gaping cunt.

My mother wondered: if there had been a man of the house, or if these men could have seen themselves owning the house, would they have been so possessive of the laundry, so keen to exhibit their virility and, ultimately, what lay beneath my mother's clothing? But because she was single, because it was the 90s, because she didn't want to be perceived as a prude and because she just wanted the job done, she never confronted them. Instead she inhabited the laundry with a detached eye, arranging magazines as she had found them like a maid tending to flowers in a vase. She bided her time until the end of the renovation was in sight, then she smuggled in her protest.

Next time the men unzipped their flies and fumbled through big-boobed farm lasses and exotic schoolgirls, they found *Building Bear* – a magazine dedicated to 'big-dicked, hairy men, working with their hands'. My mother heard no protest; the magazine was never mentioned, and the kitchen was completed three days early.

I gave the sailors the finger on each hand and went inside.

The sun had dipped and I was two bottles of red deep. My mother had refused to materialise in her dresser mirror, leaving me rambling to myself. To *hell* with friends and chefs and restaurants. Why should I bend to their norms? I was an individual! I needed more than a sales job, a husband and a limp-dick chef. And I was still young! Despite what Beth had insinuated. Why the need to grow up? Sure, I wasn't in my twenties, though I still knew how to give pleasure, how to derive pleasure. I was confident, accomplished – well, not so accomplished. And anyway, if I wanted to grow dry and sexless on this block of land that sprouted nothing but piles of shit, waiting for sailors to invade, was that not my prerogative? I'd meet the challenges head on! Snap up chairs, snap up property. Torn at the seam, splayed naked, pussy ajar.

I was playing an Al Green album on my record player, tripping around the living room, pouring myself a little Baileys – the wine all drunk – and swaying my hips in the window's reflection. Outside was black, and all I could see was myself and me, dancing with each other.

I knew I should call it a night. Knew on waking my head would pound with regret and shame. But the door was already open: the night before I'd slept, dissatisfied, with a married stranger. What was to stop me doing it again? An idea of decency? A bygone belief that two men in two nights was shameful? Beth had wanted a whore; I'd give her a whore.

Stumbling to the bedroom, I threw on a tight dress that had become a little too tight. Then I went to the bathroom and, with an unsteady hand, circled my eyes with black liner. I put on heels and inserted a finger into my vagina, rubbing the scent on my neck like it was Chanel No. 5.

I called a cab then realised it would likely take thirty minutes, by which stage I would have passed out, so I decided on meeting it on the public road as the walk would keep me awake. I poured another Baileys and stepped into the cold dark.

The bracing air accentuated the perfume of the coastal wattle. I took off down Marsh Drive, stumbling over pebbles and potholes, trying to maintain my line. I gave up and removed my heels. My house and porch light were soon out of sight, and the moon – despite its fullness – barely touched the ground through the dense canopy. Fog concealed the road ahead. I lit up my phone and shone it around. The naval bush either side of me appeared sparser at night, as if the darkness illuminated areas where shrubs were yet to grow. My eyes traversed the empty space. In, out, here, there. Until I realised I was looking at a trail leading from one side of the bush and opening again across the drive; the prohibited land was crisscrossed with thin tracks.

Wind blew, and branches groaned overhead or ahead. It was hard to discern direction. Then there was cracking but no wind, like twigs breaking underfoot.

I shone my phone to the right. The light caught something – eyes in the mist.

I dropped my Baileys and ran. My feet torn by sticks, I ran. Not daring to look behind, I ran. A streetlamp illuminated my farm gate, and I sprinted for the safety of the deserted public road. I threw myself at the gate, the cool metal against my arms and chest calming my nerves, grounding me. *Nothing's there*, I told myself. It had been a trick of the light. I held on, as if to a lover, until I'd caught my breath.

I closed my eyes, listening to moths and crickets zap themselves senseless against the streetlamp. It took me a moment to realise I could hear a car drawing close. I put on my heels and stepped nearer to the road, ready to hail the taxi. The high beams were blinding. I soon realised the vehicle was a white Commodore and retracted my hand.

The car slowed as it passed, and a guy leant out the window. 'YOU FUCKING SLUT, YOU FUCKING WHORE.'

The engine revved and he sped off. I was alone on the road once more, but this time amid the lingering smell of petrol and distant sound of a six-cylinder engine.

I no longer wanted to be there. I wanted to be home in bed with brushed teeth and clean pyjamas. I'd been foolish, an entitled brat, toying with a precipice.

I lifted my phone to cancel the taxi. As I did, the car engine grew louder – he'd turned around. Fear shot through me. I leapt out of the lamplight, smashing myself into dense bush. I bent under the wire fence and forced myself into the scrub. Blackberry brambles ripped at my dress and skin; I wanted to cry out but caught myself and burrowed further. The car slowed and pulled in, stopping at the farm gate. High beams illuminated the pathway, exposing all surrounding bushland. I buried my head in my hands and dared not breathe. I heard his car door open, boots skirting shrubs. *Let him think I'm an apparition. Let him think I'm nothing but air.*

He got back in the car, reversed, revved his engine to high hell and accelerated onto the road.

Then, skidding, smashing! A pole or tree?

I threw off my heels again and ran down the drive.

10

She'd been watching me sleep, her yellow eyes the first thing I saw upon waking. Were they the eyes from the night before? No, too small, too rounded. Her claws clasped the ceramic edge of a birdbath I'd hung from the twisted moonah outside my bedroom window. The hawk's fat feathered body overwhelmed the bath, threatening to break the bough. I wanted a closer look, though dared not move for fear she'd take flight. The morning sky was grey and foliage wet.

My head thumped from shame and last night's drinking. Though how could I feel remorse at acts abandoned and behaviour unwitnessed? I'd been destructive, yes, but had I been bad? All my envy and lust and anger and impulsivity only ever led to self-ruination. Beth insisted on responsibility, but to whom? Jung had written of this shadow self; would he have locked me up, left me to rot in the Department for The Beast Within?

I'd run all the way home, stumbling in the dark. I couldn't remember the last time I had run such a distance. My body rejected the adrenaline, frothing wine and Baileys into an acidic shake, so that as I pushed my key in the front door, I turned around, gripping the verandah's rotting rail, and spewed up the night.

Once inside, I locked the door. In the shower I curled naked against the cold tiles as steam and scalding water wrapped around me. Blood and debris from my feet and arms washed down the drain. Bringing my knees close to my chest I buried my head and closed my eyes. I had done the same thing as a child, often imagining I was a mermaid and the shower a cave heated by thermal springs; my mother, a distant banging on the door, would yell that I was late for school.

That night I managed to make the world disappear again behind fogged and frosted glass. There was nothing but me and the rhythm of falling water. Anything could have gone on outside, but there, in my metre-square aquarium, all I knew of existence was that it was warm and wet.

The morning's reality was of no such comfort. I should have been relieved – only *I* had witnessed my stumbling, swaying, cold desperation, yet this somehow heightened my embarrassment. As if self-abasement's cathartic release was denied without public humiliation.

I shook out my limbs to shake my thoughts. The hawk seemed to mimic me, shaking rain from her body, then opened her wings and took flight. I leapt from my bed and stood at the window, staring skyward as she rose out of sight across the sea. My feet stung and my evening's dress lay irreparably torn and crumpled upon the floor. The hawk was right; it was breakfast time.

In the kitchen I heated a slice of frozen bread in the microwave until it resembled a warm pillow, then covered it with butter, Vegemite and slices of gouda before zapping it for another twenty seconds. My mother used to make this dish for me as a child, cutting the bread into quarters. I'd place each triangle in my mouth, chew it side to side then dribble it onto my palm and roll it between my hands until it formed a ball. With the four balls in a precise row on my plate, I'd savour them, nibbling each one.

I took the bread intact to the verandah. The wind caressed my face as the rain dripped onto the corrugated roof. The overhead gutter was missing, so water fell like a beaded curtain around the house. I reached out, attempting to part the flow with my fingers.

Peering over the verandah railing, I could see that mud had consumed all evidence of my self-loathing. I was struck by a hangover realisation: I wanted to be witnessed – seen. Relief at not having had an observer to last night's mania was eclipsed by my loneliness. I missed my colleagues, clients, even Fran and her vandalised attire.

It was time to emerge into the world again. After breakfast I popped four Panadol, ironed a shirt and pants, dragged myself to the local library and printed my CV. When driving the not-so-deserted Hill Pass, I made sure to ignore the view from my side window of a smashed car covered in police tape.

Fifteen minutes from home, I arrived at an end-of-the-line regional train station. It comprised a wooden bench, a single streetlamp and a leaky awning under which two people sheltered. Parallel to the train tracks was a muddy road littered with puddles and potholes. A large dirt carpark snuggled between the road and tracks, and on the other side of the road stood a collection of converted barns and a century-old coolstore, which was the size of a country football field and once used for preserving fruit. Painted above the coolstore

entrance a faux age-distressed sign in cursive writing read
'Antique Market' but really meant 'Junk Yard'. The market
was a popular tourist destination and the only home on the
peninsula to antiques (if one could call them that), though I'd
never cared to venture there before.

Arrows were staked throughout the compound and
pointing in all directions. Jumping puddles, I followed one
to reception in the main building. When I opened the door,
a twee brass bell sounded overhead. Musk filled the air and
cobwebs the windowpanes. I was standing in a graveyard of
retro Tupperware, Victorian lace and second-hand romance
novels – not even Geoffrey Browne's Collectables Department
would sell such gimcrackery.

A squat woman in capri pants and a parakeet-print blouse
emerged from behind a partition. Her hand was wrist deep
in a packet of Twisties, and the winter scarf draped across
her shoulders was the only evidence she wasn't on a beach
holiday.

'Morning, love,' she said, cradling her snack. 'How can I
help?'

I slid my CV across the desk. She retrieved it with her
free hand, sucking the other clean as she read. 'Marsh Drive,
Hydra,' she said, dropping the CV an inch below her eyes.
'Locking up your pets at night?'

'Excuse me?'

'Near the naval base, the wetlands nature reserve ... the
address you've typed?'

I mumbled something about the recent move and how I
didn't own pets, though if I did I would adhere to all council
regulations.

'Never mind,' she said. 'Local yarn.' She continued reading, taking a seat on a torn leather swivel chair and twisting side to side. The chair squeaked with every turn, threatening to collapse under her.

The doorbell rang and a couple entered holding a rose parlour lamp with crystal pendants.

Parakeet Blouse dropped my CV to coo over it. 'My nanna had one just like it,' she said, producing an A3 pad of paper maps and floor plans like one may find at a tourist centre. She circled an illustrated building in red and ripped the map from the pad. 'Exit back through the door and turn left,' she said as though directing them through an emergency ward. 'Go to barn number two – the number's on the door. At the cash register ask for Tracey – she's the best dealer for antique lamps. Don't forget: barn two, Tracey.'

The couple left, and Parakeet Blouse returned her attention to my CV.

'We don't have any more space to let,' she said to me. 'And anyway, there's a five-year waitlist. We're up to our eyeballs in dealers.'

'I don't have to be a dealer. I could do admin, cash register, clean.'

'Sounds like you want my job.' She gave back my CV, putting a hand on her hip. 'And from what I've just read, you're overqualified for that.'

'But no one else wants me!' I admit that I said this to garner sympathy from the shrew, yet as the last syllable dripped from my lips, I knew it to be true. I was tainted by too many bad judgement calls, and there I was, in the arse-end of antiques, choking back a tear.

But it seemed to work: her stance softened. 'You moved here by yourself?'

I nodded.

'No friends, family?'

I shook my head.

'Poor love, bet it's isolated in that reserve ... I've good intuition, you know, can always tell when a possum's broke its tail. Alright, I could use an extra pair of hands at the front desk; I've an obligatory trip fast approaching.' She appeared to grind her teeth. 'And I'm sure our dealers would value second opinions from time to time – hell, you're more qualified than them!'

She couldn't pay much or offer many hours, but I didn't mind – I was rolling in relief.

Parakeet Blouse was now known as Gemima, the market's manager, administrator and bookkeeper. She reported to town council and a board of retired locals. 'But between you and me,' she whispered, 'I'm head honcho.' She'd been terrorising the antique market for over twenty years, and if I 'stuck close' she'd show me all there was to learn from the chintzy compound.

Overwhelmed at where I was and having finally found work, I wanted to hug her, bludgeon her, bury my face in her enormous breasts. Instead I cried.

'There, there, love,' she said, coming around the desk to rub my back. 'I've a good feeling 'bout you! Just down on your luck, that's all. And look what's happened – you asked the universe to deliver and it gave you a job. That's what the universe does, you know,' she was looking me dead in the eyes, 'gives to those who ask.'

I wanted to ask about starving children, infertile couples

and quadriplegics, but all fight was gone. I leant into her soft, comforting chest.

'*Oh*, you'll be right.' When my tears cleared, Gemima handed me an emu-feather duster, the kind belonging in French-maid porn. 'Dust a bit, get your bearings, then meet me here.' She drew a red asterisk on a floor plan of the warehouse, tapping it twice with her pen. 'The café. Midday.' She ripped the paper from the pad and gave me the A3 page.

I looked over her shoulder to several hanging signs that pointed to the café.

'I've always wanted a co-conspirator,' she said. 'Let's see 'em try to argue with me now I've got you in my corner.'

I wasn't sure who 'em were or the nature of the disputes I was expected to partake in.

After nearly a hundred days, numerous false starts, one reputation in disrepair and a sunken inheritance, I'd secured employment! I danced through the coolstore, duster in hand. I was feeling frivolous, free. I could be anywhere in the world; no one knew where I was – well, no one from my real life: no parents, no husband, no friends, no colleagues. I was new-girl Anja, who came from nowhere. I had no history, no context and no providence. I could do as I pleased! Was I still drunk?

The rain had ceased. I threw open the door and jumped in a shallow puddle, then pirouetted in the dirt and almost tripped over.

Looking up I saw a phone booth hidden among large pines. I couldn't remember when last I'd seen one – perhaps in London – they'd mostly been decommissioned in Australia. The glass windows were covered in graffiti. I moved closer. Pine needles littered the floor, undisturbed; no one had stepped inside for some time. I swept them away with my foot. Was the booth still in operation? I lifted the heavy orange handset and placed it to my ear. There was a weak dial tone. I retrieved my mobile and found her number, then slotted a dollar into the machine. Keys stuck in their pad as I dialled.

'Hello?' said the distant voice.

I was silent.

'Hello?'

…

'Hello? *Hello?*

I hung up. I could do as I pleased!

By midday the delirium had passed and I was bathing in mellow contentment, aware and grateful a huge load had been lifted. It was this notion of lightness I chose to focus on, ignoring my lightly nagging head, which was seesawing between an enduring hangover and repulsion at my obscure surroundings.

My midday rendezvous with Gemima was at the back of the coolstore in a quintessential country café. Wooden tables were covered in red-and-white checked cloths and covered once more with plastic protectors. Each table had a serviette dispenser, glass salt-and-pepper shakers and a miniature vase holding a daisy. The two waitresses wore yellow American-diner style uniforms with white aprons and large button badges depicting a sketch of the coolstore's façade.

Gemima was sitting alone at a table with a bowl of pumpkin soup and a glossy tabloid. I sat opposite her, and she pointed at the bikini-clad celebrity snapped on her summer vacation. 'Tries too hard, that one,' Gemima said, then handed me pen and paper and launched into the induction. 'The dealers all rent floor space. There's fifty-two of 'em competing for the sale. Though they don't see it that way – but that's their problem.' She buttered white bread and dipped it into her soup. 'Your biggest concern is memorising dealers' locations and specialities – who sells toys, who sells linen, blah-blah-blah. It's all written in here.' She slid a worn address book towards me.

I considered mentioning my Essence and Archetype Classification System but thought it best not to make too many changes on my first day.

'When potential sellers come to the front desk, as you saw this morning, they want to know which dealer can best off-load their goods. It's *your* responsibility to point them in the right direction.' She took a sip of soup. 'And if their item can be sold by more than one dealer, then it's *your* responsibility to give them those dealers' information; they can barter percentages themselves – that part isn't your problem.'

Gemima's induction appeared to be a series of issues that either were or were not my problem.

She leant over her soup and lowered her voice. 'If, however, there's a potential seller who could go to either Marie or Josh, I always neglect to mention Marie. I'll let you make up your own mind about her, but just between you and me, she's a busybody.'

I nodded gravely.

A waitress arrived to take my order, and Gemima introduced her as Clara. Clara and Gemima were around the same age, though Clara had a warm smile and well-defined calves. I pulled out my wallet and counted coins.

'First meal's on the house,' Clara said, placing a reassuring hand on my shoulder.

Had Gemima spread word I was down and out, a figure due pity? I ordered a sausage roll.

'Good choice,' Clara said with a wink and returned to the kitchen.

Gemima continued spilling coolstore secrets. 'The café ladies are first to arrive in the morning. That Clara's pretty proud of her lemon slice.' Gemima gave me a knowing look. 'But it's got *nothing* on mine! I'll bring you a piece. My mother's recipe, nothing compares! ... Though don't let Clara see you eating it – she's prone to fits of jealousy.'

I struggled to imagine the waitress in a fit of jealousy.

It was dark and nearing dinnertime when Gemima and I locked the coolstore. She paid me in cash – 'To get you on your feet, possum' – and told me to return in a couple of days. Light rain was falling, and the road had turned to mud. She sheltered me under her umbrella as we walked towards the two remaining vehicles. I waved goodbye from inside my car as she drove off into the night.

Alone in the carpark, I turned on the radio and crooned along with love songs as I stared out at the desolate train station. It was a pitiful sight, but I wasn't ready to return home; I was scared to – worried I might repeat last night's solitary cycle of drink and remorse. At the same time, one should celebrate one's triumphs. Breaking a three-month unemployment drought was an accomplishment. I fingered the cash in hand: not a fortune, though an adequate amount for a pleasant dinner.

When I started down the road in search of a restaurant, I had no intention of returning to Goostronomic. *Leave it to fate*, I thought. It just so happened that fate drove me back, and why not? I'd been sheepish when last there, scatty when people asked my occupation. I had avoided those conversations, deflecting to Beth or saying I was 'self-employed', a 'freelancer'. Now I didn't have to lie, could be myself entirely. My life was crowded in solitude; this was a chance to dampen the silence.

I pulled into the gravel carpark. Chops and Dice meandered over, and I rubbed their woolly coats until they lost interest, realising I had no food. I could see the hostess through the rounded glass door. Rebecca, I think her name was? I waved, and she tilted her head as if attempting to translate a foreign tongue.

'Oh, Beth's friend,' she said as I grew closer. 'Did you forget something?'

It was a relief to be remembered. 'Thought I'd join for dinner. You see, I have some celebra—'

'I'm afraid we're fully booked.'

'Can't squeeze me in?'

'No, there's nothing available.'

'For a fellow local?'

'Not without a reservation.'

'Perhaps something in the back? The chef's table?' I moved among the circular chairs and rounded diners.

'Um. No.' She edged in front of me. 'No, we can't do this evening. It's, it's not possible.'

I was shocked. Had I really made such a poor impression? 'The treatment was certainly different when Beth accompanied me.'

'Without a reservation there is nothing I can do.'

'I see space, empty tables.'

The hostess lowered her voice, clearly aware eyes were upon

us. 'It's not appropriate, okay? His wife is here, and, look, I know what he's like, but she's a nice lady. Please don't cause a scene.'

I wanted to laugh but didn't. 'I'm not here for *him*, I'm here for food! For friendsh—'

'Please.' She put one hand on my back, the other on my arm, and turned me towards the door.

'No!' I shook her off as I return-served the word. 'No! I want to celebrate. I just got a new job. It's been three months and, and I'm employed!'

Our waiter from two nights earlier recognised me and came to assist.

'Tell her!' I said to him, pointing at the hostess. 'Tell her I just want to celebrate.'

'You can't be here.' He grabbed my other arm and they both held on, escorting me from the building to the carpark.

I looked behind as they dragged me out. The restaurant was a sea of bends and curves. Round eyes and round heads with round gasping mouths.

I jumped into my car, reversed and accelerated, tears streaming down my face. Gravel sprayed into the air as I whacked the car into a black mass – *Please don't be Chops, please don't be Dice*. I tore out of the drive.

My celebratory dinner was a downhill affair. Fried rice and lemon chicken in an empty Chinese restaurant overlooking a shopping-centre carpark.

That night I dreamt of an ocean, waves battering a ship, my body rocking here and there, the smell of blood and hay and salt. Sirens blaring, wind knocking at a porthole, and men, dozens of men, looking over me, devouring my body with their eyes, hands running the length of my back, my stomach and inner thighs, hands in all directions, invading all crevices. I opened myself to them, wider and wider, till I was lost, torn apart at the seams, each man taking a portion for himself, pocketing me away like a lost button. The joke was on them, though: I turned to water in their hands, wetting their black velvet shoes.

I woke at six to a text message from Beth: *STAY AWAY FROM GOOSTRONOMIC.*

It was still raining. The bedroom windowpane was frosted, and sunlight was breaking over the scrubland. I wrapped myself in a blanket and went to light the cast-iron fire in the lounge; I emptied a basket of wood and newspaper into the furnace and struck a match. Flames showed promise but quickly tore through the kindling. I slipped on my uggs, wrapped the blanket tighter around my body and, carrying the wood basket, opened the front door.

A pool of blood lay at my feet. I gasped, choking on the sudden intake of cold air. The crimson liquid trailed in a thin line from the front door, across the verandah and down the three wooden steps. There was a thumping – once, twice, thrice – coming from my bottom stair. I shuffled forward into the blood and peered over.

Once twice thrice.

A mangled rabbit knocked a back leg against the bottom wooden step, its neck gashed open and spurting gore.

Once
twice
thrice.

I twisted around, looking here, there. No one. Just rain.

Descending the steps, I scooped up the wild animal. It froze at my touch, dying instantly, a final squirt of blood drenching my mohair blanket. Its pink eyes rolled back in its head.

Another gift. Territorial sailors, or had Noah slaughtered the bunny as vengeance? Was he watching from the shadows? I was exposed and on display, fruit for the picking. *He'll think I'm quite mad if I don't yell and scream and hide. Is that what he wants, a trembling woman?*

I wrapped the rabbit in the blanket and placed it in the wood basket. At Hydra's failed veggie patch I dug a thirty-by-thirty centimetre hole and buried the creature in the rain-soaked mohair, then took one of the ceramic stakes I'd bought to signpost my plants and wrote, 'Warning, dead rabbit.' I stuck it between the desiccated basil and coriander.

I wanted to claim more – wanted to leave additional marks, to tell the story. I took another stake, this time writing, 'Warning, bold crap', and thrust it next to the patch of scrub I'd flung shit into weeks earlier. If I were to drop dead, I'd want people to know that I had been there, that memories pervaded the property. So I took a final stake, writing, 'This is where Beth left me', and jammed it into the earth where her car had stood.

[ITEM 7]
17:00, 14 September 1985.
Recording: Two-way Transmitter between Base &
Cottage.

Lieutenant, come in. Over … Lieutenant, are you
there? Over … Hello? Lieutenant, can you hear me?
It's Chief Cook Dixon — I'm sending someone with
your tray now … Not too sure what you'd prefer …
I'm going to take a punt and give you the lasagne
… Is that okay? Hello? … Enjoy, Sir. Out.

[ITEM 8]
21:00, 14 September 1985.
Interview — Archives: Lieutenant Brendan Quartermain & Professor Colin Tatterson

BQ: Professor Tatterson, you're a hard man to lock down.

CT: History never sleeps. Thank you for meeting me so late [tea being poured]. Milk?

Thank you.

How are you enjoying our base, Lieutenant? I hope you're not feeling too isolated out there on the Western Peninsula — or as I like to call it, the Wild West.

It's further from the township than I would have liked … and I've had my dinner delivered two nights in a row now.

I see Captain Morrissey is steering you clear of the British.

It would appear so. There is, however, something to be said for inhabiting an area of incident … The arrangement has allowed for undisturbed exploration. I've now been to the shooting range and safety school. But Professor Tatterson, why were you unavailable for interview earlier in the day?

Ah yes … I'm not sure if I should say this on tape — please rewind if you find it compromising — but we couldn't meet earlier as I'd caught word of an underground memorabilia sale: Australian Naval equipment from the Vietnam War. Anyway, it's all off record, but the navy sends me to underground and unauthorised sales. I'm not there to report anyone or ask questions, just to buy the memorabilia.

To what end?

Officially it's for the archive, but I have a sneaking suspicion — and again, please rewind if you feel this is damaging — that by removing items from the public market, I'm subsequently raising the price of wartime memorabilia.

What does the navy care about commercial supply and demand?

There's a theory in academic circles that the higher the cost of Defence antiquities, the higher the rate of national patriotism. And the higher the rate of patriotism …

The higher the rate of enlistment.

Bravo, Lieutenant! But that's a very cynical and conspiratorial way of looking at our employer.

[laughs] Aside from unofficial and off-record collecting, what are your other duties?

Aside from the cloak-and-dagger stuff? I conduct historical research, retain the collection and the archives, and run tours for the public.

Petty Officer Gibbs informs me that he returned an item here.

I have a medal from Officer Gibbs, but 'returned' is an interesting concept. If Officer Gibbs had stayed long enough to listen to the history of the precious medal he so valiantly saved, rather than storming off on his vendetta, then you would both know that it has never formed part of the archives.

It's a fake?

Oh no, very real. But it's the first time that I or anyone stationed here has seen it — well, other than those around when it first landed on our shores.

May I take a look?

Be my guest. [inaudible]

This is a United States issued medal!

It's curious, someone as patriotic as Officer Gibbs not even recognising a foreign badge.

So there was no theft?

Not from this building. But I must admit that I'm intrigued by it. The medal is over forty years old. It's unlikely, albeit not impossible, that it was buried under the shooting range this entire time. The rust does reflect this theory. And, if this were the case, I can surmise that perhaps it came across the Pacific in '42.

With a visiting convoy?

The Yanks were stationed here at ███ for six months. They liked our proximity: close to Japan though far enough from the front to safely host visiting admirals and work with our boys on a joint ballistics launch.

What can you tell me about the medal?

This is the fun part. It's an Expeditionary Medal, awarded to US officers serving on foreign soil, primarily against armed opposition.

Why the smile?

Well, we were their allies! There was no armed opposition in Australia, which makes me think it was awarded for its secondary purpose: for when an officer is deemed to merit special recognition … and for which service no campaign medal will be awarded.

A classified operation?

Known colloquially as the Clandestine Medal.

Let the record show that Professor Tatterson winked at me.

Before you go, Lieutenant.

Yes?

I've lived here twelve years now, and I've learned that men on the base … they're prone to yard arm clearing.

There's a culture of blame-shifting?

In a manner of speaking. I simply wonder, then
— are all these incidents you're looking into
linked? Sometimes people see what they want to
see. It's easier than living in the truth, living
with oneself.

Dead animals aren't vapour, Professor.

Certainly not, but what I mean is: don't go
hunting ghosts, Lieutenant, they simply don't
exist.

---

*A note to the reader: Item 8 of the report has been omitted.

11

I'd been accepting cash in hand for three weeks, and aside from occasional poor customer relations, I'd proven myself rather adept at memorising the coolstore's history and distributing goods among the retailers, whom I now mostly all recognised by name if not by face. There was little use for my appraisal skills, but I was grateful to once again spend my days among furniture and other items; however poorly they were preserved or unremarkable their make, they were still objects with history, and I enjoyed meandering through stalls with feather duster in hand, imagining bodies that once slouched here or made promises of love there. I'd regained my footing: it wasn't Sotheby's, or Chiswicks, or Geoffrey Browne, but it was a good place to hibernate, a jail in which to lick the wounds.

My colleagues, I concede, were warmer than my Geoffrey Browne family had been. What they lacked in style they made up for in inquiries and concerns – the antithesis to Lawrence's approach – and I didn't need to skirt their questions. When asked if I had a partner, I'd reply 'no' – it was simple. And when asked why I'd left the city, a quick 'my mother died and I wanted a change of scene' would suffice. There was neither lie nor cover up. I was fresh as clean linen.

I was also aware that less attention was paid to my attire and that I would have stood out wearing the clothes I'd usually worn at work in the city. I gave up on blazers and crisp shirts, and left my hair to hang loose around my face. The only adornment from my old life was the Léa Stein brooch that had graced my blazer on my last day at Geoffrey Browne. I wore it now as a talisman, a reminder to never again confuse snakes with ladders.

While I appreciated my colleagues I still preferred to lunch by myself, often eating in my car, which I'd park overlooking the station. The train would arrive each day at 12.03 and depart at 12.25. Usually just a few commuters would disembark; on other occasions the carriages were empty. Once I saw a woman, my own age, sitting still in a carriage with apparently no intention to detrain. Odd, considering the station was at the end of the line. *Has she nowhere to go?* I thought, consumed with pity. And then the thought – *Perhaps she's a train-yard spook.*

Each lunchtime I would guess the number of passengers to disembark. If I were correct, I'd treat myself to a call from the derelict phone booth. 'Hello? *Hello? The* fuck is this?' she'd say. Surely she had realised by now that the calls were coming from the purgatory she'd placed me in. I was surprised at how stupid she was, totally lacking intuition. The past fortnight I'd averaged three calls a week. Yet not once did my name slip accusatory from her tongue.

That lunchbreak, I bit into a chive and chicken sandwich – Clara constructed a delectable sandwich – while waiting for the train to arrive. I guessed two passengers and crossed my fingers.

There was a distracting knock at the car window. An elderly man in a woollen jumper and corduroy pants was gesturing for me to roll down the glass. I'd seen him around the market and taken him for either a dealer or a Bertie – either way, his sudden appearance was a bother.

'Colin Tatterson,' he said, extending his hand into the sanctuary of my car, 'one of the compound's many peddlers.'

I recognised the name and shook the large arthritic mitt.

'I've been informed,' he continued, leaning on the car door, 'that the girl assisting Gemima and the girl who bought at the naval base are one and the same.' He possessed a gappy smile and the not unpleasant smell of shortbread.

'The rumours are true,' I said, wondering at his angle.

His eyes livened with the confirmation. 'Visit my corner sometime. You may find something of interest.'

The train rushed in, the din of braking wheels pausing our conversation.

'Ah yes,' I said. '"Mu-Sea-Um" – clever.' Referring to his boutique, which specialised in peninsula history and naval memorabilia, especially that which came from HMAS *Hydra*. One passenger. 'I'm afraid I'm not as seafaring as my recent purchase may have you think.' Two passengers – *close the doors.* 'I simply liked the view.'

'And the solitude?' He presented a folded map with a red circle around his barn. 'Building three,' he said, as if I hadn't spent the past three weeks memorising store locations.

I put the paper on my lap so as not to obscure my view of the station and continued staring straight ahead. *Close the doors, close the doors, close the doors.*

'Well, history never sleeps,' he said, waving adieu and finally shuffling off.

The train whistled and started up. A third passenger jumped from the sliding exit. *Crap!* I'd been itching to make that call.

At Geoffrey Browne the week would crescendo with an auction. The compound, however, didn't run to the same tempo – there was no weekly fever pitch. Even on Sundays, the busiest part of the week, life moved to a slower beat than it had at the auction house. Some stallholders didn't even bother appearing every day, assuming their neighbours would take care of any transactions and pass on the proceeds.

I told myself that more freedom was to be found in this new role. I wasn't hemmed in by auction dates and arguing with departments over the distribution of objects. One could contend I had assumed a role comparable to Lawrence's, in that the distribution of the objects stopped with me. Over time, I believed, I could convert the compound to classifying objects through essence and archetype: the Department of Nostalgias for Marie, the Department of Practicalities for Josh.

I did a test run on this theory when a customer presented for sale a bygone Royal Winton Petunia cake stand most suited to the Department of Indulgences, which I'd marked out as shop ten in the coolstore. My plan, however, hit a snag when the customer returned to tell me that while the dealer appreciated the consignment, they didn't sell china. I would need to find an alternative passage for my taxonomy.

When not fantasising about rearranging the stores or serving customers, I found there wasn't much for me to do, and I often wondered why Gemima complained about being so busy. But my years at Geoffrey Browne had done little to prepare me for the myriad of redundant questions raised by the market's brigade of customers. It is staggering how little people choose to discover on their own, always arming themselves with other people's answers. Unaccustomed to being anyone's 'go-to', I took each question as an intrusion, an attempted exposé, as if the people asking 'Where is the café?' or 'Do you sell second-hand books?' were seeking the results of my latest pap smear. Gemima seemed to pick up on my discomfort with these mindless questions, often appearing from nowhere when a customer came through the door.

That afternoon, however, Gemima failed to materialise when a customer seeking our office hours (available on the website) came to the front desk. I found my boss in barn five, eating her second packet of Twisties for the day while badgering Marie over the agreed upon size of her shop. Gemima counted her footsteps aloud as she marched out Marie's allotted area. On seeing me, she discarded the Twisties packet onto one of Marie's Victorian tables. 'Check your contract,' she said to her as she ushered me to a private corner. 'I'm going to Queensland,' she whispered when we were out of earshot, 'for a week.'

I was to be alone, unattended.

'Northern Queensland … in *November*,' she said with disdain. 'It's that sister of mine's fiftieth.' She spoke as if I had been gifted a back catalogue of her family history.

'Divine,' I said, not sure why we were huddled in a corner.

'Dreadful, Anja. It's going to be *dreadful*. Not to mention the disasters that will naturally unfold here!' She gesticulated around, and then her eyes narrowed. 'She was born in Victoria, my sister, yet she expects us all to march north in that frightful heat!' Gemima paused to smile and wave at Josh as he walked past and out of sight. 'Apparently it's some kinda lah-di-dah affair at her designer home on the river.' She tugged at the band of her capri pants. 'The heat! It's alright for her – she's skin and bones, doesn't feel a thing. I could whack her with a frypan and she'd keep standing.'

This was more than Lawrence had ever given me: a peek under a skirt woven with sororal jealousy. I was keen to partake, to foster our relationship. I knew my real job here was to appease her, make her feel heard. I've never taken well to small talk, though, and I racked my brain before asking, 'How long has your sister lived in Queensland?'

'Twenty years. *Lord forbid* she think of our mother.'

'She can't travel?'

'God, no! Has dementia, poor thing. Lives in a home. Doesn't know us from the local cat. Anyway, I'd like you to take charge while I'm gone. You're the only one I trust, love.'

An oddly intimate comment given Gemima barely knew me, but it worked. 'Absolutely,' I said, 'whatever you need.'

Truth was, though, that I was scared about her leaving. I was capable of anything and had grown accustomed to her watchful eye.

Gemima kept me late that day, detailing the plan of action. I didn't mind the extra hours – enjoyed having someone to converse with. As my next shift was in a few days' time, there was a chance that this would be my last human interaction until then; I might only have magpies and a creaking verandah for company. So I soaked up Gemima's words and focused on her pebble eyes. She seemed appreciative of the attention and the seriousness I brought to each task.

The problem, therefore, wasn't extra work – it was the hour struck on the clock. The sun was falling, night was stirring in her bed, and I'd be arriving home after dark. I'd be walking up verandah stairs that had twice betrayed me. I had decided, though, that no matter how fretful or insecure I became, I would not lose another job. I smiled tightly, listening as Gemima detailed payroll, grinding my teeth as shadows set in.

Looking back now, it seems ridiculous I didn't just move house. Most rational people would have. But at that stage in my life, I was far from rational. To leave a property after only a couple of months was to emulate the decisions of my mother's teetering mind, and I couldn't forget, even with a wage, that money was tight. Then there was the emotional investment – I'd sunk so much of myself into the land that if I uprooted now, I would become a mere shell of flesh with nothing behind the eyes.

I convinced myself that adaptation was all that was needed. There were blackout blinds in Finland and mosquito nets in the tropics, and I too could modify my living space to suit its fearsome environment. I'd started double-locking the house, parking the car two leaps from the front door, steering clear of the cliff-side chairs and sleeping in pyjamas with a knife under my pillow. It wasn't so unusual – how many other women slept clothed, head resting upon a weapon? I obeyed this nightly ritual. Tended to it sincerely and piously. I couldn't control my land, but I did reign over my behaviour.

Was I being absurd? Perhaps the gifts were nothing more than a fox kill and fox scat. There's no malice in animal acts. I, after all, had moved into *their* reserve, *their* habitat. It could also be the sailors; perhaps I'd found myself in the midst of a harmless initiation ceremony, one that would surely run its course. Or *was* Noah responsible for the slaughtered rabbit? He had fetishised the shooting and consumption of bunnies at his restaurant, made known his willingness to skirt wildlife regulations. Was this revenge at my recent intrusion? Was I being shown what happened to unwanted vermin? Though it wasn't Noah's who had loosened his bowels at my front door…

I didn't know how to solve this puzzle, so I packed it back into its box in my head.

Long after sunset, Gemima grew tired of talking and sent me home. I sped from the market's dirt carpark and turned onto the deserted Hill Pass. Up ahead, the damaged pole and last remnants of police tape had been cleared. I zoomed past the site of the crash and pulled into my drive. I was about to step out to open the gate when I realised – I was famished. There was zero food in the house, not even crackers. I hadn't been to the store in a couple of weeks, often hurrying home before dark, promising myself I'd shop after the next shift or on a day off, though on my days off I had found many an excuse to not leave the property. That evening I had no choice but to turn around and drive on.

The supermarket was near empty. A teenager at the cash register twirled her hair and flipped through a magazine. I placed in my basket toothpaste, toilet paper, milk and coffee.

I stopped at the pasta aisle. My mother had loved stuffed pasta – ravioli, tortellini, agnolotti, mezzelune, fagottini, pansotti. It was the one thing she would cook, and only when bought fresh from the market. I remembered watching her nibble round the edges like a child, saving the filling for last, a flavour bomb she'd consume with delight. By the fifth parcel, however, she'd grow bored, lose interest in eating and push her half-finished plate away.

One morning when I was thirteen, she woke me before dawn and told me to jump in the car. I would have been embarrassed to be seen in my pyjamas had the market not been empty at the early hour. The fresh-pasta man was still setting up his stall when my mother tapped her nails on the glass counter. 'Two serves of the stuffed stuff,' she said.

He jumped into action, detailing the offerings.

She raised a hand to hush him. 'Make it a surprise. Mix them up.'

At home I boiled morning tea while she cooked the pasta, pairing it with a butter and sage sauce. We sat in front of one large bowl with two forks. She nibbled all the sides, letting the hot air steam from the pockets, her mouth then opening wide to take in the fillings. 'Pumpkin. Beetroot. Beef.' She threw her hands in the air, announcing each flavour as it was consumed. We finished the bowl; it was the first time I'd seen her finish a meal. She sat back in her chair, pleased with herself, as if she'd solved a riddle that had plagued her entire life.

Whenever it was school holidays – or later, when I returned from London – she would wake me early that first morning, and we would go to the market for mystery breakfast pasta.

Under the supermarket's fluorescent lights, I chose five packets of ravioli: duck, sweet potato, caramelised onion and mascarpone, fig and goat's cheese, spinach and ricotta.

At home I parked the car two leaps from the house, double-locked the front door, drew closed all blinds, slid into my pyjamas and placed my sharpest knife under the pillow.

[ITEM 9]
10:00, 15 September 1985.
Interview — Mango Hall: Lieutenant Brendan Quartermain & Petty Officer Henry Robbins

BQ: Tell me about your work at HMAS ██████ *, Officer Robbins.*

HR: ██████'s my home base. When not deployed, I run the safety school, have done so for the past three years. I enjoy training the cadets, preparing the kids for life at sea.

You'll be aware that I've met with Officer Gibbs?

I'm aware that he requested the meeting. Gibbs is adept at linking our lives. Just when I think I'm done with him — pow! He pops up! Insistent on making everything about him, inserting himself into others' stories.

You're talking about your history together in Rockhampton?

I guess he told you. Biggest mistake of my life. Hands down. Gibbs and I deserved everything we got. And yeah, sure, I believe he saw someone down at the shooting range. But Gibbs has got it stuck in his head that all the stories are linked — that this is some kind of revenge fantasy, and we're the victims. A few environmental posters on land pillaging appear, and he's screaming bloody murder! Wants us to sue! Can you believe it? The ego! If you ask me, it's cause he hasn't dealt with his own Rockhampton guilt. Still in denial over any wrongdoing and his psyche's haunting him, playing up. It's the same as when he's out at sea — can't control the mind, weak constitution.

So, you don't agree with Gibbs in thinking this was personal?

I never said it wasn't personal. Just that it wasn't directed at Gibbs and me. [long pause]

Go on.

Look, all I can tell you is that Pepper knew it was coming.

How do you mean?

A few days before it happened, I took Pepper for a walk around the reserve. She loved it there, plenty of birds to chase, shrubs to scramble through. On particularly hot days, I'd throw a stick into the lake, and she'd dive in after it. It was a good way to cool her down. She didn't like the ocean, was a bit of a scaredy-cat. The number of times she'd swim in after me, whimpering …

Whenever 6 p.m. rolled around she'd be at the front door, wagging her little stump, leaping up and down like a clown. Boxers never really grow up, you see, remain pups for life. I'd say to her, 'Get your lead, get your lead', and she'd bound off, returning seconds later with it in her mouth. Moving her head away whenever I'd go to grab it. She liked to walk herself, you see. Seemed to take pride in it.

<u>Christ</u>. I had her since she was a pup. Well trained, better than any cadet I ever came across. She was intuitive too. Knew when you were blue, and she'd nuzzle up. When you talked to her, she'd tilt her head side to side as if trying to understand … Anyway …

So that day, I managed to secure her lead and we headed for the reserve. It's about a twenty-minute walk from the residential centre. When we got there she was running around like a mad thing, getting muddy, and I was sitting there under a tree, smoking a dart while watching her amuse herself. I'd throw the occasional stick whenever she brought me one.

There was nothing unusual about that day, or the reserve. The sun was beginning to set, and she was just her usual idiot self, you know, leaping in the air, dashing here and there.

Then the birds started squawking.

Dozens of them, bouncing on their branches and circling in the sky.

Pepper spun around. Her ears were forward, her stump stiff out, and the hackles on her spine up like she was a Rhodesian ridgeback.

'Pepper!' I yelled. 'Pepper!'

But she couldn't hear me. Whatever had made her mine was gone, had receded like her flews till she was all teeth and gum and snarling animal.

She shot towards me.

I leapt up.

But boxers are all muscle, and within a second I was struck down again. She was on top of me, gnashing in my face, and then I felt it, warm, spreading across my chest: she'd peed herself. By now she was whimpering, shaking, her eyes rounded, and she was Pepper again. I picked her up. She licked my face — the big sook — and I carried her home. She didn't stop shaking until I'd locked the door behind us in our unit and closed the blinds.

What was wrong with her?

At first I thought it was a brain haemorrhage or some kind of rabies. Perhaps she'd picked up something off one of the animals in the reserve. In the past I'd found her licking at decomposing wildlife, a guilty look on her face. Later, I thought perhaps it wasn't even me she was snarling at — perhaps it was someone I couldn't see. Someone behind me. Someone, or something.

I've thought about those few days over and over, and the more I think about it the more I'm convinced she knew something was about to happen — a premonition of sorts. They say animals can sense thunderstorms and earthquakes hours before our tech can. Maybe it's a change in atmospheric pressure, or a sixth sense; either way, something erupts in their world that is not perceptible in ours — until it's too late. It's like she was in a trance, in tune with another realm.

After the incident in Rockhampton, I started reading up on animal instincts. I wanted to know why I did certain things and how I could better myself — shift away from primal drives. I even became vegetarian — for a minute. [laughs]

Anyway, the next few days Pepper was different. She was always a cuddly pup, but she became timorous — wanted to be a lapdog, get into bed with me. I'd arrive home and find her shaking behind the couch. It reminded me of veterans I'd seen with PTSD: unable to relax, always with an eye cocked in expectation. She wasn't the same dog. Refused to go on walks or even leave the front lawn. She'd go outside only to relieve herself, and then she'd be scratching at the door to be let back in. At night, she'd stand by the window and stare out into the dark, looking this way and that, searching …

Eventually I had enough, got the lead myself and tied it to her trembling body. Dragging her from the house, I realised taking her on her usual route would be too cruel, so I changed direction and took her through another reserve entrance, and towards the safety school building. She cheered up quick smart when she realised we were on a different track. She even started wagging her stump, looking up at me, grateful.

I don't know if you've seen it yet, Lieutenant, but the safety school is really an old ship that we run drills on: gas explosions, evacuations, that kind of thing. It's where I spend the majority of my days, so I never took her there after work hours. Approaching the school, I unleashed her and threw a tennis ball into the empty ship. Off she flew. [long pause]

Yes.

The minute she was out of sight I heard her yelp. Just once. I ran towards the hull, finding her behind a rock; she'd been dragged, slashed throat to groin, her innards pooling around her …

Did you see or hear anything?

Nothing.

137

And I believe you burned the body?

Yeah. Near the lake. She liked the ducks.

Officer Robbins, what you're really suggesting here is that your dog, leading up to her slaughter, was aware of being stalked. You're implying the killing was premeditated.

Look, you asked for my story, and that's it. I know you were sent here because upper rank think it's some disturbed vigilante or cadet, but I'm telling you, this wasn't human.

You're suggesting a fox or wild dog?

Maybe. But what kind of boxer pisses itself over a fox?

A note to the reader: Items 10 & 11 of the report have been omitted.

12

I was on the phone ordering more map pads for the market when the doorbell rang and I was struck, frozen in panic, by a face from another lifetime: Miranda, Joseph Hiegel's PA, walked into the coolstore. She was wearing sneakers and jeans; at first I didn't recognise her in such casual garb, especially as an empty womb hid behind her loose blouse. She held open the door for a bearded man with a sleeping babe attached to his chest. I turned my back to them. They meandered along the counter and into the pits of the market. I hung up on the map-pad salesman and followed the lovers' languid stroll between stalls.

Every few metres they stopped and Miranda stroked her husband's back or adjusted the beanie on the napping babe, who would have been barely four months old. Was the infant stained by the stress of Joseph's death, as she had feared?

The couple fingered bits and bobs, noncommittal and not focusing in on anything other than one another as they floated through the building. There was no evidence of trauma, and it was clear Miranda's one duty now was to the child. She bent to smell the baby's head: talcum powder, fabric softener, sugar-shit?

I, in turn, smelt seaweed and rotting fish, pungent death and callous sea with no answers. I was pulled back to Greece, to our hotel on Hydra, to gazing down at a pebbled beach littered with dead bodies.

I held my legs in the air for a minute, which was nineteen minutes less than had been instructed, but I was starving and desperate for a swim. Hayden raised his eyebrows when I sat up, placing my feet on the cool tiled floor.

'What?' I said like a child caught sneaking sweets.

He knelt and lifted my ankles, rotating me back till my feet rested on the headboard. 'The beach isn't going anywhere,' he said, passing me my book and assuming the same position. 'We'll do it together.'

After our recommended twenty minutes, we walked hand in hand to the breakfast room. The hallways and reception were empty. Windows were propped open and waves crashed against pebbles below on the hotel's private beach. The smell of bitter coffee drifted towards us.

A fellow guest came storming around the corner. I recognised him from last night's dinner: an American who had been enchanted by Homer and beaten by Athens. 'Dirty city,' he had bemoaned to the table next to him. 'Graffiti, cat piss, refugees! Had to flee to Hydra for some relief.' As he marched towards us, he directed his finger at me, moving it side to side while staring at my chest.

'Is he pointing at your tits?' Hayden whispered.

The American heaved closer, forcing us from his path. Without losing pace, he poked at air surrounding my bust. 'Won't be needing those!' he said before disappearing down the hallway.

'My bathers?' I asked Hayden. He shrugged, and we continued to the breakfast room.

The buffet was laid out in the centre of a large marble room with a cascading fruit pyramid, fresh cheeses and meats, juices and bread. It took us a moment to realise that napkins were discarded on the floor, plates left half-eaten at tables, and a frypan burned empty at the omelette station. There was no chef to tend to the pan, no waitstaff to tend to us, and no guests to nod 'good morning'. Yelling came then, from the breakfast terrace.

Guests and hotel staff gathered round the balcony, transfixed on a grand event below. Some were shaking their heads with hands to their mouths; others viewed the scene through the safety of their phones. Was someone drowning?

Hayden, a confident swimmer, pushed his way through the crowd, his hand holding mine tight as if I might be lost in the breakfast mosh pit. At the front of the crowd he slid me between him and the balcony railing.

Nothing appeared amiss, and then the water frothed like lava. Were fish feeding? A large squid, the length of my arm, leapt through the air and landed heavy on the shore. Its wings flapped in vain, disturbing the coarse sand. It was followed by another and another. Dozens of squid flew towards the beach, their crimson bodies baking in the morning rays.

'There will be a pod of orcas, offshore,' said a Swedish guest, sounding confident.

I searched the horizon for a dorsal fin. Were the squid swapping one kind of death for another? Surely whales couldn't eat an entire symphony? Was there no value in trying their luck in the water, swimming away from the collective?

Every few moments another squid would leap from the ocean and plant itself on the pebbles. I'd watch its body writhe before another squid caught my eye and then another and another and another and another – an endless procession.

I remembered a news story that had come out of Ireland when I was young. A shepherd had lost his flock when one sheep was scared off a cliff by an unknown threat. Perhaps it had just been a fox or even thunder, but the whole flock followed suit. Jumped to their death. Those sheep at the bottom of the pile were ground to pulp, but those at the top, the survivors, at most broke a few bones, their fall softened by their woolly family. Their fates, though, were sealed: they were eventually euthanised. When reporters asked the shepherd why he had decided to cull the surviving flock, he said it was because they no longer acted like sheep. They kept their distance from one another, refused to communicate, looked at their fellow flock members in horror. 'It was no way for a sheep to live,' the shepherd had said, 'they'd be picked off by foxes.' He raised a fence near the cliff's edge and used insurance money to buy a new flock.

There was still no sign of any dorsal fins.

'Has this happened before?' 'Will they stop?' 'When will the beach open?' 'Someone do something!'

The concierge, wide-eyed, held up his mobile as if it were a beacon. 'The Fisheries Department will call at any moment.'

'Can we swim?'

He shook his head. 'That, I would not advise.'

The guests grumbled.

'But I can offer complimentary aperitifs at sunset!'

The appeased guests dispersed towards the breakfast room.

Hayden squeezed my waist and moved with them, yet I stayed put a moment longer, scanning the ocean, desperate for those dorsal fins.

Children were gathering on the sand. One picked up a squid and threw it back into the water; another did the same. 'Κολυμπήστε! Κολυμπήστε! Swim! Swim!' the children cried. But no matter how many they threw back to sea, the squid kept flying towards them. The children screamed and kicked at the creatures, then took run-ups and booted them back to the water, and when that didn't work they stepped on the writhing squid, twisting their shoes back and forth until the wet bodies split. Hayden's semen dripped into my bathers.

Inside, most guests had returned to their tables, and the omelette chef was making a show of cracking eggs. The room, however, was quieter than usual. A depth of thought had descended, and guests smiled silently at each other as if to speak would only serve injustice to what had been witnessed. At the same time, through gesturing at a neighbouring table, guests could pretend this was just another buffet breakfast.

Hayden was reading the *Financial Times* and half through his sardines on toast by the time I sat. A waiter, younger than us with thin arms and wrinkled eyes, came by the table offering traditional Greek coffee. I accepted, and he instructed that I skim froth off the top before sipping.

Hayden leant across the table and held my hand. 'I put a baby inside you.'

I took his hand to my mouth and kissed each one of his fingers.

'If there's no beach action,' he said, 'let's catch a ferry to one of the neighbouring islands.'

I agreed to his plan, and after breakfast we headed to an island thirty minutes north. Unlike Hydra's white, cream and beige stonework, the buildings there were painted pastels of cyan, mustard and pea-green. Superyachts crowded the marina, and Armani-crested couples walked hand in hand along the jetty.

We found relief from the day's heat at the air-conditioned Archaeological Museum. Ceramics and jewellery spoke of past worlds, though what excited me most were the bathtubs: grand stone slabs, any of which could work in a modern home. They were so like our current baths that I couldn't help but sneak a touch, rubbing my hand along the smooth marble rim as an ancient bather would have done, in a time near impossible to perceive.

After the museum we strolled around the marina shops, assistants on our tails, eager to point out their wares, often holding jewellery to my neck. 'How beautiful she is, how beautiful, you see the colour, it matches her eyes, colour of the ocean,' they said to Hayden, who nodded with a tight smile. The guilt from not buying anything soon overcame us, so we retreated for lunch, trekking inland away from the port, its tourists and overpriced food.

We climbed backstreets until we saw a sign pointing to a taverna. It was a quaint stone building with a few wooden chairs and tables out front. We sat down, and a short man in a white singlet came out with a carafe of water and two menus. He waved his hand over his face, indicating how hot it was, and we mimicked his actions. When he left I put down the menu and stared out at the cobalt-blue water below the restaurant's cliff edge. I had a sudden urge to make love to

Hayden, to pull him from the table and drag him down to the rocks below, tearing off his clothes until our skin on the hot rocks and the Aegean sun moved as one. I lifted my leg under the table and danced my foot towards his groin.

We ordered grilled eggplant and zucchini, fried sardines, tomato salad and herbed rice wrapped in vine leaves. We washed it down with a carafe of wine.

After lunch we climbed down the rocks and shed our clothes. Hayden dove into the refreshing cool of the water. I, never having learned to dive, climbed down a rickety ladder drilled into a rock. We did not make love. On the return ferry to Hydra I ran my fingers through his hair, pulling out salt flakes.

When we arrived at the hotel there was a line at reception, twenty cursing-guests deep, all with packed bags. The concierge had his hands raised, trying to calm the herd as he offered a complimentary night's stay.

'I came to this *godforsaken* island for a beach holiday! Beach!' screamed the American. 'False advertising. I'd die touching that water. Refund! Refund!'

Hayden and I looked at each other and headed towards the balcony.

The smell – pungent and decayed like a fisherman's offcuts – reached us from inside the breakfast room. I gagged a little. We covered our noses with our t-shirts.

Hundreds of squid, flapping or lifeless, lay below. Some had turned white cooking in the sun; others kept on coming, one after another, after another. Squid as long as my torso, others no bigger than my hand, some with bulging eyes and some with tentacles fine as hair.

'I'll find a new hotel, first thing tomorrow,' Hayden said.

On the beach, three old ladies dressed in black were taking their hands to their lips and spitting at the ground, making an exaggerated, '*Ptu, ptu, ptu,*' noise as they opened and closed their fingers.

'They are spitting, at the Evil Eye,' the thin waiter behind us said.

I hadn't noticed him standing there, and the sudden strange voice was alarming.

He presented a tray with two small glasses. 'Your complimentary aperitifs.'

That night I dreamt of my mother. She gasps for air. Cheeks hollow, features contorting. White skeletal arms raised high, pleading. Breath thin, squeak. Then dribble, dribble, dribble, saliva down the chin. Water spilling the airways, pouring out the mouth, torrents of ocean. A tsunami.

The next morning there was no one at breakfast. The omelette chef stood alone by the gas fire with nothing to cook. Morning sunshine had hit the squid hard, and the smell was now thoroughly infiltrating the breakfast room. Staff had done their best to quell the stench, lighting mosquito burners in each corner of the room. Rather than smother the reek, this merely added another element of complexity to the foul bouquet.

I left Hayden at a table with his coffee and went outside to see if squid were still throwing their bodies ashore. Wrapping my sarong around my lower face, I saw that both nothing and everything had changed. The new day's light illuminated a beach that had doubled in squid since the night before. I knew then, it was nothing short of a disaster.

Two men in linen business suits were at the balcony railing, pointing at the squid and surveying what appeared to be a map of the Aegean and Mediterranean. One man looked over at me. 'We will sue!' he said. 'They've cost my hotel €20,000!' *Sue the fish?* He pointed straight out to sea and then at his map, landing his finger on the Libyan coast, grinding away at it like it was a cigarette butt. 'I heard reports, a sinking vessel – Libyan – pouring toxins, pollution, into the sea. That's why the squid come, that's why they kill themselves.'

The other man spoke. 'Last night at the taverna, men were talking of this vessel, but nothing on the news stations. It's a cover-up! Always a cover-up.'

The hotel owner whacked the map with the back of his hand. 'I will demand they make payment to me.'

I scanned the ocean: no dorsal fins, no tanker or sinking vessels. The Libyan coast was too far for the naked eye to see. I wondered if there was someone in Libya right then, staring across the water, demanding Greece compensate for their misfortune.

I went inside to join Hayden, who was staring at a plate of untouched eggs. Another man was sitting in the otherwise empty breakfast room; he had chosen to sit at the table next to us – safety in numbers. He had his laptop open and was engrossed in whatever he was typing.

'I've been thinking about Crete,' Hayden said. 'We can catch an overnight ferry —'

'I want to stay.'

He looked perplexed.

'There's more to the island than swimming,' I said.

The waiter came over with my coffee and a grave face. He appeared thinner and wrinklier than he had the night before.

147

'It's Fukushima,' he said. 'Nuclear fallout. The fish have been exposed, and soon we will be too.'

'That was years ago,' I said, 'and Japan is many oceans away.'

The waiter shook his head. 'It's the beginning of the end,' he said, pouring the coffee with a deathly expression.

'And what is your end-of-days plan?' Hayden asked, with a sarcasm that didn't seem to penetrate.

'I will go back to Athens,' the waiter said, 'be with my family, get off this sick island – well, if they let me; if the hotel closes. We still have three guests!' He looked at the sole traveller, then back to us before walking off.

'Does that satisfy you?' Hayden said, turning to me. 'Even the staff want us gone!'

'I can't explain it, but I want to stay – need to stay. To see what happens, to know why it's happening. Is it human error, the ocean, the squid themselves?'

'That's exactly how I feel,' said the man at the table next to us. 'In fact, it's why I'm here.'

Dr Martín González was his name, a marine biologist in his fifties from Catalonia. He had travelled to Hydra as soon as he heard that squid were suiciding. He wore a torn vest and aged leather boat shoes. His head was shaven, perhaps to hide a receding hairline, and he had a deep resonant voice and a dazzling smile.

He informed us he was functioning on very little sleep, was relishing the coffee in his hand and had been sailing all night to get here.

'Who sent you?' asked Hayden – always a pragmatist, always keen to suck dry the juice from any citrus. 'Which organisation do you work for?'

Dr González worked for himself, funded his own research, travelled where the work was and published independently.

'You're retired,' said Hayden, laughing.

'It sounds magic,' I said, mostly to myself.

Dr González looked at me. 'Perhaps I can interest you in conducting an experiment this morning? Care to assist?'

'She's an antiquarian, not a scientist,' said Hayden.

'Then she has a good eye. And after my lack of sleep, I could use a good eye.'

I was thrilled, consumed with a thirst for knowledge that I couldn't recall having since my first days at Sotheby's. I turned to Hayden, my eyes wide with excitement.

He sighed and shrugged. 'It makes no sense, but whatever.'

I told Hayden I'd meet him for lunch at a taverna we'd discovered when trekking our first day on the island. It was a romantic, secluded eatery with its own olive grove and views of the island's southern coast.

I was late to lunch. Hayden had finished eating by the time I arrived and had few words to say about his morning, nor was he interested in discussing mine … though I was. I spoke free and fast about dissecting squid, sampling their organic matter – living and dead. I'd also carried out water testing and mineral sampling from the seabed; I told him that results should be back the following day. Did he know the squid had only marooned on the 500-metre stretch of beach outside our hotel? The rest of Greece – the rest of the island – was free of the phenomenon. Did he think that was significant?

We decided to meander into town for a drink. It was quieter than usual. Cobblestones sounded underfoot; donkeys and their riders overtook us on the path, carting food, toys and nappies from a recent shipment. The handlers whipped the animals mercilessly. Hayden and I walked hand in hand, an intimacy we usually avoided during the heat of the day. As we came down the hill to the port's commercial centre, I spotted a store with a collection of Evil Eye jewellery. I let go of Hayden and placed a €500 necklace to my skin.

'For protection,' the shopkeeper said, 'very beautiful.'

'It's more expensive than a night in our hotel,' Hayden said.

'Can't you see?' I whispered to him. 'Most of the tourists have left. We should help out where we can ... and there's something not right on the island – can you feel it?'

He left the store and I paid for the necklace. I found him standing by a jetty, the midday sun beating down on him, his neck burned red. 'We'll ruin our holiday if we stay here.'

'How is it ruined? We're eating well, talking to locals.'

'Our hotel smells of death. Admit it, you're revolted; it's unpleasant to be around and yet, you want to stay? I don't get it. It's not our problem, Anja, it's not our business or our responsibility. We have not been charged with finding their solution.' He kicked a wooden pylon. 'And why do you even care why it's happening? Even if you understood the riddle, there's nothing you could do about it!'

I took his hand in mine again, and we walked to the end of the marina, where a group of fishermen were smoking and playing cards. We paid one of them twenty euros to take us out to sea, letting us swim freely far from any squid.

The next few hours were spent diving in and out of the water, baking our bodies on the boat's bow, and rubbing salt from our legs and eyelashes. When the fisherman saw the blistering of Hayden's skin, he said it was time to return, and shared with us fresh watermelon his wife had cut and wrapped in muslin.

We arrived at the hotel as the sun was setting. The lights were out and the corridors dark. We slipped past the thin waiter, who was crouched in a corner with his face in his hands, and went straight to our room, tearing off our wet bathers, leaving them to drip, drip, drip into the bathtub as we slept naked under cool fresh linen, the necklace snug in my collarbone.

We slept until dinnertime, when there was a knock at the door. Hayden rolled over and stumbled to the bathroom; I threw on a dressing-gown. It was Dr González – the results had come in.

Later I was leaning against Hayden, helping him button his shirt for dinner, when Dr González's words spewed out of me like cheap wine. 'The water has been found to be more acidic than usual.'

'Is that right.'

'Yes, it's reading nine on the pH meter, and that is very high.'

'What should it read?'

'Well, I don't know exactly, but I do know it's not usual.'

Hayden remained silent.

'And … and after dinner … I have to go with Dr González. He's measuring all the levels again, wants to know if there's any change in the pH when the sun is down.'

'*Jesus Christ*, Anja!' Hayden tore away from me. 'We're here on holiday together, you're in the midst of ovulating, and your sole interest is in this bloody squid quack!'

'I just need to know. Once I know, then I can concentrate on the holiday.'

'Anja, there's no answer. This is it. This is *all* there is. And these fucking squid will keep coming and you'll *never* understand why, but that's okay because it's not your job to know.'

I moved to hold his hands, and he pushed me away.

'I feel like.' He cleared his throat, suppressing the break in his voice. 'I feel like I'm dragging you down a path where you have no interest in going, and I'm sick … I'm sick of fucking tugging, my arms are tired.'

'I'm sorry, I'm sorry, my love.' I went to him and hugged him and kissed his fingers, his sunburn and face. I inhaled deep his smell, told him it would all be alright, no more tugging. We made love in the shower, on the edge of the bed. All the while I thought of the squid, their bodies contorting in the sun, and after cumming I fell into a deep sleep. I barely heard cupboards open or suitcase clasps snip shut, and when I awoke at three, he was gone.

I popped a contraceptive pill I'd smuggled into my bag, sat by the open window until daybreak and lit one cigarette after another. If he had caught the last ferry to Athens, I thought, he'd be at the airport by now, waiting for a plane back home. Perhaps he was already in the sky, looking down on the Aegean. Or perhaps he was still at the marina, only twenty-reachable-minutes away, awaiting the day's first ferry to Athens.

There, in the quiet of the empty room, I realised that what had caused the squid to kill themselves was of no interest to me. It was the conclusion I sought: an answer, a bookend, knowing that the circle closed for a reason.

At sunrise I heard men yelling below. I went down to the beach, no longer bothering to cover my nose and mouth.

Great tractors were lifting squid, carting them away. The ocean was still, forgiving; nothing flew upwards from its depths. The men on the tractors wore industrial masks. Where had the equipment come from? Were the machines always on the island or had they arrived especially by ship for the clean-up?

'Who is removing the squid?' I asked the waiter. I hadn't seen him but knew he was standing behind me.

'Institute of Marine Wildlife,' he said. 'They study a few and bury the rest back out at sea.'

A garbage tanker appeared from around the corner and made its way to the beach.

'And Dr González?' I said.

'Gone. His work is done. He said he can only research while squid are suiciding. Once they've stopped, it's as if they never started. The ocean shows no trace. Hides no clues.'

'Did he discover why they were doing it?'

'No, it's a mystery... but for my sake, I hope they never return. I was certainly on edge with them around, not myself at all.'

'Yes,' I said, unlatching the necklace and handing it to the waiter. 'I think we can all say that.'

Miranda appeared before me. 'Do I pay for this here, or at the front desk?' she said, holding a balding vintage teddy bear and ripping me from my past life.

'That counter,' I said, pointing to Tod, the distributer of second-hand toys and germs.

'Thanks,' she said, walking off.

There was no flicker of recognition. Had I changed so much? Perhaps her memory of that day had tainted her recollection of me, morphing me into a chair-thieving succubus dripping in rage and desire. She purchased the teddy bear and floated out the door.

13

Fleshy arms rose from behind a silk screen. Half a dozen dealers, Clara from the café and I gathered in silence as Gemima moaned and groaned, squeezing herself into a dress she'd purchased online for her sister's birthday.

The dress was delivered to the coolstore, for what Gemima insisted were security reasons – 'Nothing is safe on my verandah, not even gumboots!' – but which also provided her a convenient captive audience. Everyone was aware the dress would be arriving that week, and when the package appeared, she announced her fitting over the loudspeaker, ensuring anyone not preoccupied with a customer felt obliged to participate in her reveal.

She emerged from behind the silk screen with a sweaty brow and an exposed back. Her bra strap was twisted, and fat rolls, refusing to be smoothed out, rumbled down her body, undulating suspect moles.

The dress didn't fit; it wouldn't even zip up. My semicircle of colleagues fidgeted – some lowered their eyes; others bit their nails. Gemima turned round and round, jiggling her behind and blowing out her stomach, ensuring we all received a clear view of where the garment refused to traverse.

One brave colleague stepped forward. 'Perhaps the designer didn't anticipate such a grand bust?'

'Size sixteen!' Gemima cried. 'You don't have small titties at size sixteen!'

We all nodded and agreed.

Marie put up her hand. 'If you like,' she said, 'I could let it out here.' Pointing at the hip. 'And add a panel to the back?'

'You'll do no such thing!' Gemima said, swatting Marie from the dress.

I tried, and failed, to imagine Lawrence parading half naked in front of his employees, flaunting his less than perfect features. He simply wouldn't do it, wouldn't let us peep behind the moss. But displaying her bumps and growths didn't make Gemima vulnerable. Waving them in our faces, she made clear it wasn't her body at fault, it was the designer – never mind that she had purchased the dress unmeasured. I was struck with a wretched thought: *Is Gemima the pin-up woman for body positivity?*

Her rage at the dressmaker and news that her sister had invited a loathed cousin to the party had sparked her into a fury such that I had previously not witnessed. I was later informed that it was to be expected whenever Gemima had word from her sister.

She threw herself again behind the silk screen as the rest of us stood in silence, listening to the fabric rip in two. The groans ceased, and we began to disperse. Josh, perhaps to lighten the mood, said, 'How about that sheep attack!'

My stomach bubbled. I knew instantly what he was referring to; I had been trying to forget the thud on the car, placing it in a sealed box in my brain that had just been wrenched open.

To my list of shames – china smasher, chair robber, coccyx breaker – I could add 'sheep killer'. I felt like throwing up, my breath tightening.

My colleagues replied excitedly; apparently everyone had heard the unfortunate tale.

Josh turned to me and frowned. Could he read my thoughts? Know I'd chopped Chops? He must have mistaken my guilt for confusion, as he elaborated on the story. 'Last month, some divorced woman hit Chops, one of Goostronomic's sheep, with her car!'

'*Burp* … Excuse me,' I said, covering my Judas mouth.

'Gross, ha? Rumour has it,' Josh continued, 'the chef there, Noah Burns, slept with some down-and-out woman – just once! – then wasn't —'

'*Burp* … Apologies!'

'Um … Then wasn't interested in seeing her again, and so the woman ran over Chops. Broke his leg!'

'That's it?' I said. 'I mean, Chops isn't dead, just broken?'

Josh looked perplexed. 'Well, it isn't great news for the sheep! He'd be shot if he were on a farm.'

This was the antacid I needed, and any thoughts of throwing up on the 70s shag rug rapidly dispersed.

Another colleague piped up. 'I heard the chef is married – a real sleaze. Doesn't want his wife to know, so can't press charges.'

Then another colleague. 'They can't inform Animal Protection either, as the chef shoots rabbits on sight without a licence – exposes the restaurant to too much scrutiny.'

'Anyway,' Josh said, 'apparently this slapper is totally unhinged!'

Hearing about myself in the third person was rewarding. I'd never heard unfiltered what others thought of my behaviour, and I imagined this to be what it's like to witness one's own funeral. How many fraudsters have slunk into their wakes, disguised under scarfs and glue moustaches? Were they able to tear themselves away? Or, like Narcissus, did they drown in their reflections? *One more story*, they'd bargain with themselves, until the costumes came unstuck and they were recognised – the jig up! *Not today*.

'Sounds like the bastard got what he deserves,' I said, walking away.

'That's one way of looking at it,' Josh murmured, 'if you forget Chops.'

Evening was approaching. I packed up my counter and went in search of Gemima, finding her buried in paperwork at a table in the dimmed and empty café.

She raised her head as I approached. 'I've done well by you, haven't I, Anja?'

I was taken aback; had I done something to suggest otherwise? I told her I was happy, that the job had given me a purpose when for so long I was wading in the deep.

She seemed to like this answer. 'I've given you a ladder out of the pool. I try to do the same for my sister, you know. But she still treats me as a fuddy-duddy. I know what she's thinking – that I'm no fun! But we can't all go gallivanting around the country, you know. She's always trying to *push*, that sister of mine. Push, push, push. She did so with our mum, got away with whatever she wanted, never listened to anyone. But you're not like that, are you, Anja? You understand that when there's a system, a smoothly oiled machine, then you'd best adhere to the way things are, not go reinventing the wheel, altering procedures and methods.'

I shook my head, though I wondered how well I'd fit in the hole she'd dug me.

'Good to hear, possum, I know I did right by picking you.'

I wished her goodnight and drove home, arriving just before dark, and when the sun dipped, I double-locked the door.

It wasn't just my work life that was flourishing; to my delight, my vegetable garden had begun to resprout. It appeared that the dead rabbit had enriched the soil, its guts and blood breathing new life into my plants.

I had the morning off work and was determined not to let the garden slide back into decay. To protect Hydra from the saline breeze, I purchased a canvas windbreak from the local hardware store and two-dozen dead mice from the pet store. I decided on storing the mice in the freezer and planting one every few days to appease my carnivorous crop.

After making a cup of tea, I donned my neon-pink gardening gloves to prepare for the morning's toil. Bees were tending diligently to newly flowered flax lily and banksia under the November sun. I breathed deep the perfumed air; I had luxurious seconds of calm ahead of me before I'd have to go to work and then to return, to adhere to the nightly ritual.

I unrolled the windbreak canvas and inserted metal poles into holes in the cloth. Heaving the poles upwards, I took my hammer and beat them into the soil. Now protected, Hydra looked not unlike a ship set for sail.

I held aloft two mice. Hydra's three heads seemed to wag like dog tails. I knelt over her body, digging two holes in the soil near the stern and bow. I placed the first dead mouse, a calico-coloured critter, in the stern-side grave and buried it with dirt. I lifted the second mouse, soot coloured with a white belly, by the tail.

That's when I felt them upon me: the eyes. I froze. The stare pressed into me, into my guts and chest. Should I stand and run? Continue digging? I decided on rising, then walking slowly, calmly back to the house, arming myself with sharp objects before the eyes realised my awareness.

I stuck the trowel into the dirt, rose and turned, the mouse still in my hand. The beast came at me. A red rage of saliva and teeth faster than anything I'd seen in my life. It sprang, and I braced myself for a tussle, biting, mauling. Death?

Fur and air brushed my face. The fox leapt over me and the dinghy, bolting for the other side of my property and back into the nature reserve. The white tip of its tail darted through wattle and was gone.

A *ssscccrrreeeaaammm*. Piercing. Shaking. Devastating. Came from the side of the reserve from which the fox had fled.

My arms locked. Dozens of birds shot to the sky as the carnal sound raged on. I scanned tree to tree to tree, searching for the source of the miserable shriek. I wanted to die, to curl up in a ball and rip off my ears.

And then, silence. Only the birds' warning calls remained as they circled overhead.

I sprinted for the house and double-locked the door. The frozen mouse remained in my hand, fingermarks depressed into its body.

Police Report
Case Number: JJ-7939
Date: 1 November 2016
Reporting Officer: Detective Greg Skelley

Incident Type:
Road Accident, run-off-road departure

Address of Occurrence:
Corner of Marsh Drive and Hill Pass, Hydra, VIC, 3920

Driver:
Justin Walker: Naval Officer, male, 36

Witnesses:
Benjamin Murphy: Taxi Driver, male, 72
(Potential unknown): female, approximately 25 – 35

Evidence:
Totalled, white, 2006 Commodore Sedan, numberplate JUS-001 (found at scene)
Damaged streetlight pole
Skid marks on Hill Pass, corresponding to where the vehicle left the road
Emergency Service phone call by Mr Murphy
Smashed bottle of Jack Daniel's (found in car)
Blood alcohol reading of 300 mg/dL (Mr Walker)
Medical Records describing stable injuries compatible with such a road incident (Mr Walker)

Mr Murphy Witness Statement, taken the night of the accident:

On 7 October 2016, at approximately 01:15, Mr Murphy, travelling down Hill Pass on his way to Hungry Jack's, came upon the vehicle wreckage. Mr Murphy parked and ran to assist Mr Walker, who was unconscious in the driver's seat. Smelling a fuel leak, Mr Murphy decided to remove Mr Walker from the vehicle and unbuckled Mr Walker's seatbelt through the rolled-down window. Unable to open the driver's door, Mr Murphy then pulled Mr Walker through the driver-side window. Mr Murphy dragged Mr Walker a safe distance from the car and phoned Emergency Services.

Emergency Services arrived on the scene at approximately 01:40 and took Mr Walker to Bunyip Emergency Hospital.

Mr Walker Vehicle Driver Statement, taken on his awakening from a three-week induced coma:

On 7 October 2016, at approximately 01:00, Mr Walker, travelling down Hill Pass, returning to his house in the HMAS *Hydra* township, drove past a woman at the edge of Marsh Drive, whom he believed to be in distress. She appeared to be 'swaying, intoxicated'. He noted that she was wearing very little and was worried for her safety: 'dolled up – a good-looking thing – shouldn't be alone at night on a deserted road'.

After driving on a few hundred metres, Mr Walker decided to turn the vehicle around to see if she needed assistance. On reaching Marsh Drive, he found the woman had vanished. His high beams spotlit the driveway, but there was no one to be seen, nor did anyone answer his calls. Mr Walker gave up, did a U-turn and accelerated back down Hill Pass.

It is here that Mr Walker's statement becomes fanciful. It's important to mention, at this stage, that on the night of the seventh a deep fog had set in on the marshlands. It is my belief that this, in combination with Mr Walker's high blood alcohol concentration (300 mg/dL has been known to cause delirium and unconsciousness), caused the accident.

This report finds that Mr Walker either lost consciousness or experienced an alcohol-induced hallucination, causing him to slam on his brakes, skid off the road and hit the light pole.

According to Mr Walker, however, within seconds of performing a U-turn and accelerating, he was forced to slam on the brakes: 'It was Anaba! Standing in the middle of the goddamn road … I'm not mad, man, I know what I saw! People been talking 'bout her for years and there she was, just like they all said – her yellow eyes shooting my car's high beams straight back at me.'

Police Action:
Mr Walker will be charged with driving while intoxicated and damaging council property.

14

The scream had burrowed into my ears and sliced a path of panic to my chest. I held on to my bedroom dresser, shaking the mirror with both hands. '*Mum? Mum?*' I pleaded, as if I thought that by conjuring her, conjuring the fanciful, I could convince myself that the scream had been rational. If my mother were to appear, I would be given my quota of the mystical for the day, and then what I had just perceived as an unworldly threat would be no more than one open to reasonable explanation.

But my mother did not appear. No matter how tightly I held the mirror – calling her name, slumping to my knees with my head against the glass – no glimmer, no ripple of reflection could be summoned. Confirming a horror: the scream, as carnal as it had sounded, was not of the body.

I'd done what I could to protect myself from the threat of men. I'd created the ritual, abided by the ritual. I hadn't escalated the issue by contacting the police or the naval base. I'd taken everything in my stride. But perhaps I had blamed the navy men and Noah because they were easy targets, obvious suspects. What if the threat was other, obtuse, transcendental – potentially even in my head?

No! No, there was an explanation for the shit, the rabbit, those eyes caught in my phone light and that grotesque cry. By constructing them into something other-worldly I was playing to type: seeking mystery, revelling in the preternatural. I'd already lost my husband. Now my land? *No more!* It was simple: if the scream wasn't human, then I hadn't heard it; it had come from my brain, a snap in the synapse. And if it *was* human ... then I'd find those villainous vocal cords.

Outside the sun was smothered by clouds, and the birds had ceased their warnings. I had one objective: to find evidence – a boot print, a discarded cigarette – proof against my madness. I stepped into the scrub and within moments was in another world, blanketed by low-hanging moonahs, she-oaks and blackberries. Light failed to trespass here, and mushrooms sprouted in the dank soil. Ahead, a private property sign flickered, and as I moved towards the yellow beacon, I held tight the cool wire, walking the perimeter as I had done my first week of possession. My eyes remained fixed to the ground, searching for signs of man.

Twigs snapped under my foot – I knew if someone was there, they would hear me. I was exposed and unarmed, though I no longer cared. Fear exhausts and eventually bores; one can't hold on to it forever. *Let there be a showdown.*

I scanned the ground and canopy, the thickets and decayed fallen trunks. Each flora, chaotic in its own way, showed no evidence of displacement. The bush was like a rococo relief: scrolling and curvaceous, dramatic and untamed. Everything uninhibited until ... ahead ... the emerald shoots of a wallaby grass parted unnaturally, as if something lay at its roots. I moved closer. Breath held tight in my mouth.

Flies circled. Innards pooled. A tongue hung loose from a broken neck, and eye whites had haemorrhaged. The crimson fox wasn't hard to see, despite attempts to bury him under dirt and bark. This wasn't the proof I wanted, but now I knew – I was dealing with something unhuman; I was sharing my land with an other.

Beeeeeeeeeeeeeeeeeep.

My phone – a reminder to get to work. I pulled the device from my back pocket. It fell to the ground. Up ahead, shrubs shook.

I fumbled with the phone, grabbed it, ran through ferns, banksias and wattle, each plant snatching at the exposed skin of my arms. In the clearing I jumped into my car and sped away down the drive.

This had gone on long enough. I needed to confide in someone: Hayden, lost; Beth, missing; Gemima … protective, maternal Gemima. I was suddenly overcome by the thought of her smothering warmth. She didn't tolerate many people, took issue with most, yet she showed an affection for me. I wasn't naive – it wasn't me per se, it was my damaged nature. She'd acknowledged as much on our first meeting: 'Can always tell when a possum's broke its tail.' Relationships are transactional, and I couldn't have cared less for the details of the exchange; I wanted to be held tight against her large breasts and comforted as if she were my wet nurse.

At the antique market I parked hastily and ran inside to find her. The front desk was unmanned, and a pink Post-it was stuck to the computer screen.

Dear Anja,

Back in two weeks.

Keep them honest.

Gemima xxx

'*Fuuuck!*' I screamed, ripping off the note.

At the payphone I dialled Fran's number. No train had arrived, no game had been played with fate.

It rang.

She answered.

I was silent.

'I know this is you, *Anja*,' she finally said, 'and when I find where you are hiding, I'm going to smash you like you did the Susie Cooper.'

I took a deep, blissful breath. 'Then,' I said, 'like Mrs Hiegel, you'll be shitting from atop an inflatable doughnut.' I hung up, lighter, appeased and then proud; it occurred to me that I hadn't heard china smash in a couple of months.

I spent the afternoon tending to Gemima's list of chores. The duties helped to quell my mind, and the phone call had mellowed my soul. Returning briefly to an old life had grounded me in a knowable, understood reality far from the innominate lurker on my property.

As I readied my desk for the day's end, hoping to arrive home before sunset, I was overcome by the feeling that a messenger – a Hermes – was about to cross my counter. It was as if some higher knowing had taken hold, although I wasn't then sure if I had always been especially 'in tune' or if my mind only remembered predictions that transpired. I was in the midst of reassuring myself that I didn't have foresight when someone walked in the door and shook my world like one would a snow globe.

He held his badge in front of me and announced himself. 'Detective Skelley. I'm looking for Anja Harley.' He was a tall, imposing man with hooded blue eyes. His glare tunnelled into me, sweeping away any good until I was nothing but regret and shame.

'Me,' I said. 'That's me.'

'Ms Harley, I have a few questions for you. Is this a good time?' He moved forward until we were both touching the counter.

I was going down: stalking, pranking, sheep chopping, coccyx breaking. It was all over red rover. My colleagues' heads appeared from behind their stalls, while customers edged closer, hoping to catch a guilty tongue-slip.

'Do I need a lawyer?' I asked.

His eyes narrowed. 'I certainly hope not.' And the thin corners of his mouth turned upwards. 'This is in regards to a car accident occurring the night of the seventh October, near the corner of Hill Pass and Marsh Drive.' He leant across my counter until our eyes were level. 'I believe that drive leads to a property owned by you?'

I had thought the crash, the predatory driver, my regretful night of drink out of my life and hadn't brooded on them in weeks. Detective Skelley had just shattered my well-constructed memory box. The driver, his words – *you fucking slut, you fucking whore* – his smashed Commodore; the defective slice of time I'd cut away was now reattached and festering.

'Yes,' I said. 'I saw it – not the crash, I mean, the wreckage.'

'That night, where were you around 1 a.m.?'

'Bed.'

'You're certain of that? It was nearly a month ago —'

'Strict bedtime.'

'Aha … You didn't happen to be out on the road?'

'No.'

'Hear the crash?'

'No.'

We watched him drum the square-cut nail of his index finger six times against the counter. *Drum, drum, drum. Drum, drum, drum.* 'A witness,' he continued, 'a taxi driver, informed me that he was on his way to pick up a passenger from your address and take them downhill.' He scanned my face – my features hardened in place. 'When, at the last minute, the job was cancelled, he decided to continue anyway and buy a burger at the local Hungry Jack's. Instead he stumbled across the crash site.'

I said nothing, ignoring every itch in my body that was screaming to be scratched.

The cop leant further across the counter until we were intimately close, kissably close. He lowered his voice. 'The crash victim —'

'Is he dead?'

'No. Stable. Though well done, guessing at his sex.'

'Fifty-fifty.' I dared not rear back, kept close, lips parted.

'Aha.' He continued in a near whisper, 'The crash victim believes that as well as spotting a woman on the road, he saw something else – or, rather, someone else.'

I was silent again, not from guilt but anticipation. My stalker that night had been in plain sight: not a figment of my imagination but a corporeal entity, seen by another – a drunken arsehole other, but a witness nonetheless. I had only to reach into this cop's head and retrieve the answers to the mystery holding me captive. 'Someone else?'

'In a manner of thinking … Does "Anaba" mean anything to you, Ms Harley?'

I looked at him quizzically.

Raising his head, he surveyed the market. 'I believe you recently purchased the property?'

I nodded.

'You might not yet have realised, Ms Harley, that we're a community of tale-bearers. And sometimes, our folktales turn from fables to excuses.'

Was he leading me into a riddle? Tipping me upside down to crack my head?

His smile became a yawn. Three molars were capped in gold. 'Thank you for your time, Ms Harley.' He slapped the counter and turned to leave.

'Wait!' I called out. 'Who is Anaba?'

He faced me again. 'Ms Harley, my job is to solve mysteries, not to perpetuate them. Have a good day.' As he opened the door, he raised his hand as if reminded of a point. 'And Ms Harley?'

'Yes?'

'The woman who phoned the taxi … most likely a sailor skipping curfew, hiding a few kilometres from base so as not to be caught. There's probably no need to worry, if you were in fact worrying. I imagine she changed her mind about going downhill. She wouldn't have been the first woman to rethink a late-night trip there.' He paused. 'We all get a little lonely, do things we regret. I doubt she'll be seen on your property again.'

He walked out the door and into the evening sun, ringing the bell for the last time that day.

From the entrance window I watched the sun dip behind the train station's lone shelter, and as the darkness grew so too did the realisation that my property was mise en scène to local folklore, the staging for some unspeakable horror Davina had neglected to mention in her deckchair fantasy.

I had been so desperate to start afresh and flee the city that I hadn't asked what had come before. Who had owned that discarded Reebok sneaker? Why was the navy selling the land or rather leasing the freehold? And who was Anaba? A ghost, a poltergeist, the spirit of some goldrush child drowned in my ladderless, unmanned cove? *An-a-ba. An-a-ba.* Three breathless sounds, as easily made sucking air in as out.

When one has been cut adrift and there is nobody left to confide in, it's easy for the imagination to go feral, especially if one is already prone to such thinking. I tried to suppress my concerns, thinking instead of Beth: practical, PP250 Valet Beth. She was adept at grounding her thoughts. And then I realised that this wasn't entirely true, that Beth had her own conflicted relationship with reality. On school camps she would gather us by the fire and tell tales of the 'grape wanderer': a lone man, draped in a black oilskin coat and leather slouch hat, who walked the rows of her family vineyard. He'd been spotted on their property for generations and only ever by women born into the family. Initially he was thought to be a vagrant who'd set up camp in the surrounding bush, yet as the decades wore on he never aged, and no one could get close enough to question him; he'd disappear behind vines and sheds when anyone approached.

According to family folklore, Beth's great-great-aunt had been the first to see him when she was playing hopscotch as a child, though it was Beth's grandmother who had seen him the most often. Once she was hanging laundry in the rising sun when she spotted him walking between rows on the horizon. She ran after him, yelling, 'Excuse me! Excuse me!' He looked at her and then was gone, not seen again for fifteen years, when Beth's aunty Heide had glimpsed him while she was making love with a visiting fruit picker behind a boulder formation.

Beth had never seen the grape wanderer, although for many years she'd scanned the vines for his protruding black hat. She'd told me seeing him was the one thing that would make her believe in the supernatural and that she would remain a non-believer until this occurred. It was a self-imposed torture. She'd spent her childhood jumping from behind trees, running to glimpse him through windows and staying out in the cold – 'Just a little longer!' – until the sun set, waiting. She wanted to believe, was begging to believe, but she couldn't make the leap until she had proof. When she was younger, after spending a whole day outside on the hunt, she turned on her grandmother, yelling and screaming, accusing her of lying. Her grandmother, though, held fast, cradling Beth as she cried, and promised that one day she too would see him, even if it took a lifetime.

Although Beth never admitted it to me, I knew she believed that until she spotted the wanderer, the secret of the vines – secret to a successful harvest – would elude her. She was afraid to inherit the vineyard without the sighting. It was as if her family's heritage were wrapped up in a man who may have been a vagrant, may have been a ghost, may have been a collective slip of the imagination.

Beth had even grown jealous of her aunty Heide's stories. At dinner parties I'd seen Heide enchant the crowd with her encounters: 'Twice it's happened. First behind the boulders, then on the morning of my wedding. I was stepping into my dress when I saw him outside the window.' In Beth's retellings of these stories, however, Heide grew more and more lascivious, flaunting her naked body at the window and on a rock for all to see. Beth would describe how Heide, on seeing the black-hatted figure, became so consumed with fucking the fruit picker that listeners wouldn't have been surprised if Beth had said her aunty had mounted the ghostly vagrant in an act of third-dimensional lovemaking.

I'd noticed that Beth's later versions of the stories were less concerned with the ghost than they were with shaming Heide. But I didn't know why the woman was subjected to such scorn – was it because Miles had never held Beth down on a boulder?

Heide believed that the grape wanderer had appeared at transitional times in her life: the loss of her virginity, and her marriage. The vineyard was to go to her brother, Beth's father, and Heide thought the wanderer had appeared at events that reminded her the farm wasn't hers – as if he had transpired to see her off, wish her well. Likewise, Beth's grandmother had seen him after a devastating house fire and when her father had succumbed to cancer. Beth's ghost had come at moments of transition and vulnerability, and so had mine. Did ghosts only come for the porous?

That night I set a trap – for Anaba, for me? I stayed late at work, arrived home after dark and drove to the furthest corner of the clearing, parking as far as possible from the house. The air was still. Stars shone in a cloudless sky. Nothing snatched me on the dark walk to my verandah nor was I accosted, taking my time to unlock the door.

I retrieved a bottle of red from the shelf and poured myself a glass. Leaving the front door wide open, I walked to the wooden deckchairs on the cliff's edge. I sat with my back to the house, to the property. A light breeze kissed my bare neck. Ahead glistened that tantalisingly forbidden water. Would little drowned Anaba rise from the waves like a siren? Or would the poltergeist slash me from behind, butchering me like the rabbit?

'Thump, thump,' I said and poured another glass.

A pregnant moon illuminated the boulders and breaking water below. I stood and edged towards the cliff. The tide was on her eternal return. I sat with my legs dangling over the edge. *I could get down*, I thought, *a leap here, scuttle there*. With glass in hand I lowered myself to the first boulder. I almost expected an alarm to sound, a blaring thunder that would awaken Poseidon himself. With my backside on the rock I extended my left leg, feeling for the flat surface of the lower boulder and let myself sink down. It was easy now. I was rushing, careless. *Concentrate. Take it slow.* I crouched to find my next position and extended my leg again. My toes found space, and I let my body slide into place, but a little too fast. My foot slipped; my right hand ran over the rock, slicing on barnacles and dropping my wineglass, which smashed somewhere in the dark. I leant backwards, balancing my weight in a gap between the boulders. I turned my hand over. The moonlight illuminated a dark puddle rising from my palm. I licked it, my tongue surveying the thumb pad; the cut was deeper, longer than I'd expected. With the tip of my tongue I licked the inside of the wound and the fold of skin. As I removed my mouth, the blood – thinned from wine – pooled again.

I looked up from where I'd come. I needed to leverage my weight, but my hand was closing in on itself, cramping into a claw. *This is it.* Stranded and woozy on a rock with a ravaged hand – and my reason? Fucking ghost hunting.

Terror rose inside me. Was Anaba really to blame, or had I done this to myself?

I'd have to find another way up, one less dependent on grip. I moved parallel along the cliff face, scuttling like a crab, though the further I moved across the rocks, the higher the wall behind me rose. I was making a slow descent. I huddled on a small rock, its edges bony against my backside. My arm was covered in blood, dripping down my elbow. I took off my shirt and wrapped it tightly around my hand, which had begun to ache.

In the distance the grounded cargo ship rose rhythmically like an iceberg from the water's surface. Broken and orphaned, I was that ship. A light appeared from below her hull, then many lights, fluttering beneath the surface, dancing around her. Was she calling me? *No, enough!* The lights were mere torches from the snorkelers exploring her mysteries.

The tide had made her sneak attack, and the sand, visible before my descent, was now enveloped. I could wait there and be consumed too, or I could charge into her depths in the hope that a path up the cliff was visible from beyond my cove. I took off my sneakers and socks, tying the shoelaces together with one hand and my teeth, then hung them around my neck. I climbed backwards with a raised arm, wading into the water. The sea was frigid.

I tiptoed uneasily into the open ocean, my toes soon numb, jeans heavy. Once waist deep, I turned to face the shore. This was a view of my property I'd never seen before, a view that didn't belong to me – a view for others, as if I was looking through their lens, their perspective of me. The house, illuminated by the moon, was more ramshackle, and the grounds vaster and more shrouded by bush than I had thought.

Could I swim out a little further? I could take in the naval base, the grounded ship. I could swim out until I saw the whole peninsula: a mass of light blinking violently to be noticed. Further still, the lights of the antique market, Geoffrey Browne, my mother's lofts, my mother's terraces. They would blink and blink until all was black.

It was dangerous to dwell on this comforting thought. Refocusing on the shore, I saw that to my left there was nothing but ocean and steep cliff, while to my right – only metres away – was a small patch of sand that had yet to be swallowed. Beyond that sand, the ground was covered in marsh thicket and gradually ascended.

With my damaged hand high in the air, I struggled to keep my footing. I edged closer, closer. The water sucked back, and my toes tore from under me.

I leapt towards a rock, catching it with my undamaged hand and the side of my front tooth. The rock's jagged surface tore skin from my chin and rib cage. My tongue ran across my front teeth; a corner was missing, chipped off, another shell for the ocean. I pulled myself up and rolled off the rock onto the patch of sand. I lay down, breathing heavily, clasping my chest and laughing till my voice gave out.

[ITEM 12]
14:00, 15 September 1985.
Personal Recording: Lieutenant Brendan Quartermain

Okay … I'm currently driving through the wetlands
reserve, undetected so far … I want to know how
close I can get to the missile range and safety
school without encountering security posts … I'm
down a back road through the marsh, may have
ignored a sign or two: 'Closed road, do not
enter'. Hopefully they're not practice shooting
at the moment [laughs] … It's an overgrown track,
but there are signs of vehicles entering recently:
broken overhanging branches, tyre marks in the
mud … <u>Whoa</u> … yeah, the road is slippery, drainage
poor. I can only go about ten clicks. [thump] Ah,
shit. [car brake on, car door opening] … [car
door closing].

[ITEM 13]
15:00, 15 September 1985.
Interview — Wetlands Nature Reserve Sanctuary:
Lieutenant Brendan Quartermain & Mr Wayne Crawley

*BQ: Again, apologies for running over the … what
was it?*

WC: Long-toothed bandicoot.

*Yes, apologies. Long-toothed bandicoot. Fortuitous,
though, in that I was hoping to interview you at
some stage, so we may as well start now.*

Molly.

Excuse me?

Her name was Molly R427. She was a four-month-old
female, a potential breeder, soon to be on heat.

*Yes, I feel rotten … They're supposed to be
nocturnal, no?*

They are. She must have been chased from her resting
place. Were you driving off-road? Disturbing any
of the flowerbeds? The bandicoots create nests on
the ground, you know.

*No, no. She just ran out in front of me and …
smash.*

Aha.

… I imagine they have a lot of predators?

Snakes and hawks. But the real concern is introduced species: feral cats, foxes, boxing rabbits … vehicles.

Yes … Speaking of prey, I want to interview you regarding the death of Petty Officer Robbins's dog.

Can't say I'm too upset about it. That mutt was always in the reserve, chasing waterbirds, digging up flora, contaminating soil with her faeces. Once I found her with a blue-billed duck hanging from her jaws. Robbins had the nerve to tell me she'd found it deceased. But its bloody neck was broken! He didn't care … I can always tell when he's been in the reserve; there's a pile of dirty cigarette butts under a tree — easily swallowed by any of the animals.

I made a complaint, you know? To the Commander and his team. Put together a whole presentation too on the unique, fragile wetlands. Informed them that the reserve would soon be overrun by pests. I brought in soil samples and water acidity levels, even presented them with photos of butchered endangered species — you know the ones I'm talking about!

Do you know what the Commander told me? He said the wetlands is for the whole community. He said it may be a wildlife reserve but it's also a place for officers to picnic and walk their dogs — that first and foremost, it's a nature reserve within a naval base, not a naval base within a nature reserve. Can you believe it?

When I told them that the long-toothed bandicoot would be extinct by 2000 they told me they were more concerned with protecting the country than they were with a second-rate bilby.

The arrogance! I was distraught, moved to action, so I hung a bunch of posters around base, warning the community that we were raping the reserve. Not that it did any good; most of them were torn down. [long pause] I'm losing the battle, Lieutenant; I don't know what the future holds for the reserve, for me.

The butchered animals you mentioned … My superiors think their deaths may be linked to the slaughter of Officer Robbins's dog, a potential escalation of sorts. What can you tell me about the animals you discovered?

The dog was not the first, but she was the first that deserved it. I had hoped a greater good would have come from announcing the other deaths, but it appears the navy only sat up and paid attention when their precious dog park was affected.

Tell me about the other bodies. I believe you discovered them?

I was spraying blackberries in the western corner of the reserve — there's a noxious crop out there that has to be eradicated. Before spraying I like to till the soil and hack as much of the plant away as possible. Anyway, I'd pruned a decent amount from this one plant, and when I stepped back I realised that the vines, which were growing over a mound no taller than my hip, had been concealing an entry.

I bent down. It was a cave, man-made, with wooden beams supporting the entrance and reaching back into the dark. I knew instantly what it was.

In fact, I'd been searching for it for nearly two years. I like to dabble in fossicking, you see, and had been aware for some time that the area was rich in gemstones — zircons and sapphires, to be precise. The government bought the land in 1911, but before that it was popular with Chinese miners who'd been chased out of the goldfields. I'd heard rumours of abandoned mines in the area but had yet to discover one, until that day. It seemed thrilling — an abandoned shaft, untouched for over a century — but when I took a step back, I realised there was a winding path through the blackberries and into the cave. The mine had not been abandoned.

I ran back to my car to retrieve my pickaxe and torch. Shining it into the cave from outside, little was illuminated. There was no way of telling how deep the system ran. I wanted a closer look, needed a closer look. I ducked under the blackberry bush and crawled the worn path into the mine.

Not too far in. To describe what I saw … it was like stumbling into Hell. I couldn't take a step without cracking bones; the floor was littered with skeletons in varying degrees of decomposition. All kinds of animals too: disembowelled koalas, bodiless possum tails, 'roos without heads, their necks sucked dry. It was a gravesite — and a storage facility; the killer had flung soil over the bodies to slow putrefaction.

When I presented my findings to the Commander and his mates, they just laughed it off! Couldn't have cared less — until one of their dogs fell victim.

The cave discovery, is that typical behaviour for a fox? A skulk of foxes?

Foxes have been known to cache their dead for winter — it's a basic survival strategy. They've also been known to kill other foxes when threatened, and they are cannibalistic. But as far as I'm aware, they never kill like this. This was with pleasure, excess — a feast, if you will. But, Lieutenant, I didn't say the animal was a fox.

What are you suggesting?

Many times while walking alone in the reserve, usually around sunrise or sunset, I've felt that something is watching me. I'll turn around but there are only trees rattling in the wind. Other times I'll think I've seen things — a flash of a tail, eyes in the dark, a figure in the distance — but nothing long enough to have any kind of certainty. It's a trick of the light, a sudden fracture in my optic nerve, which fails to register clearly in my brain. Then once … and only once … I heard a piercing, soul-shaking scream when no one but I was in the reserve.

Mr Crawley, if it's not a fox, what is it?

It's another introduced species.

15

My palm had bled through the makeshift bandage and onto my pyjamas and bed linen. I had planned to wash my hair that morning, but the hand wouldn't unclaw. I stood naked in front of the mirror: busted tooth, scraped chin, greasy mane, ripped rib cage and crippled hand. In the past I would have been aghast at this new look, but I liked the truth it brought me; for the first time my dysfunction was on the outside when for so long it had been hidden behind pressed shirts and a Léa Stein brooch. I may have been a wreck, may have imagined a ghost, may have been utterly alone, but I was not yet forsaken – I had a job. It was the one thing tethering me to the world, keeping me from sliding into the ocean again. I wrapped my hand in another t-shirt and made an appointment with the downhill bulk-billing doctor.

Aside from my Chinese dinner a month back, I hadn't explored the supposedly seedier side of the peninsula. The main street strip mostly consisted of a warehouse pharmacy, discount outlet, bakery and empty stores. I walked past a trio of vacant shopfronts that had clearly once been a café. Davina was now plastered on the middle window. She wore the same cobalt-blue suit and posed her hands with their bangled wrists and manicured nails as if to ask again, 'Can I tempt you?' I wondered at the shopfront fantasy she sold there.

A portable sign on the footpath pointed to the doctor's clinic down a side street. The waiting room was full and it was not yet 9 a.m. I sat among sex workers, methadone users, and a teenage boy in baggy pants, biting his cuticles and sliding his heel in and out of a crusty sneaker.

After a forty-minute wait the doctor called me into her surgery. She didn't seek an explanation for my state or offer sympathetic words; she merely unwrapped the ratty t-shirt from my hand and announced, 'Stitches!' with a little too much enthusiasm. The wound was lacerated to the muscle, she informed me, and then admonished me for not coming in earlier.

At the basin she washed debris from the cut then ran iodine over the open flesh, holding my wrist tightly as I squirmed and moaned. She frowned as if disappointed by my weak pain threshold. 'Guessing you'll want a local?' she said, pushing a needle into the exposed muscle.

I wanted to faint.

'Buck up, I've seen worse.'

Although numbed, I was grossly aware of a great deal of tugging and avoided looking at my hand, sipping water as she sewed it back together.

She then washed my chin and rib cage with more iodine and produced a rubber band, pulling my hair into a topknot. She told me to treat myself to a blow wave.

The tooth, she said, was a separate issue. There was nothing she could do other than inform me that it was a clean break with no exposed nerves. The only reason to visit a dentist was aesthetic, and this was only to be considered if I had private health – I did not; it had lapsed in the months since Greece.

I was reminded of a conundrum faced at Geoffrey Browne, concerning an inlaid ivory jewellery box: exquisite piece, 1870s, Anglo-Indian. A fragment had been chipped from the ivory head of a twisted teardrop from the central buta motif. Faulty pieces were usually repaired, but how to treat missing ivory, likely from a gunned-down elephant? Replace tusk with tusk? Highly unethical, potentially illegal. Engage an artisan to counterfeit with shell or china? Would forever alter the authenticity and potential value of the item. Or leave it be? Disfigured and exhausted, though retaining a faithful beauty.

'You could always go gold,' the doctor suggested. 'Cheaper than porcelain veneers!'

At work I greeted my colleagues with my new chipped smile, ungroomed hair and clichéd explanation. 'I fell,' I said, waving a bandaged hand in the air. I knew it was dramatic, but I didn't have the energy to explain my midnight experiment.

It was 11 a.m. by the time I arrived. Apparently the morning had been busy, and Josh had needed to step up to the counter, but I'd missed breakfast and needed sustenance if I was going to get any work done. I thought it best not to be seen eating in my car after only just arriving, so I pulled up a chair in the corner of the café.

Clara finished prepping in the kitchen and came to take my order. 'Some spill!' she said. 'Can I get you a cold pack?'

I thanked her and declined, saying it all looked far worse than it felt. I ordered a chocolate milkshake and tuna melt. She rubbed my arm and got to cooking.

I leant back in my chair. I was unaccustomed to garnering sympathy – not that I'd ever before been host to such a disfigured shell. It was a pleasant feeling, one not felt in many years. Sure, people had worried *for* me, but this was different; this was approached with tenderness.

Clara returned with the drink and two melts. 'Eat yourself healthy,' she said, rubbing my back.

I was gulping down my shake and first sandwich with unabashed delight when naval sycophant Colin Tatterson appeared by my side – the man had a real knack for infringing upon personal time. 'I came as soon as I heard,' he said, pulling up a chair. 'Ruth from coins and stamps told me you were in a rumble.'

'What? I told everyone I fell!'

'That's quite unbelievable. You must confide – was it someone from *Hydra*, from base?'

Did I want to embroil the sailors? I could say it was an attack in the dark. First a turd, then a carcass, then a brawl – a natural progression. I took a sip of chocolate milk and let it spread across my tongue. As tempting as the lie was, I'd tangled myself into too many webs. 'I wish I could condemn another,' I said, 'but for these injuries, I have only myself to blame.'

Colin put two tanned, arthritic hands on the table. 'I can help, Anja. I have sway there, or did … once upon a time.'

The insistence was draining. Even if I had been attacked, his approach was fumbled, too forthright and unlikely to lead me to surrender. 'Listen, Colin. This. Was. Me.'

'Victims tend to blame themselves,' he whispered.

'*Jesus.*' He was relentless. 'I was hunting Anaba, alright? I was on a little ghost hunt and then fell down the rocks at the front of the property.'

'Anaba?' He straightened his back. 'What do you know of Anaba?'

'Bloody nothing, apparently.' I shoved the melt into my mouth.

'Well, this has certainly taken a turn.' A smile broke across his face. 'You would have known if you had troubled coming by my store.' He patted my head, 'Drop by after close. I'll be waiting,' and left before I had time to swallow my mouthful and decline.

This had all come a little too late. Anticipating an exorbitant dentist bill had grounded any lofty thoughts, and I no longer cared for the ghost named Anaba or why locals appeared so mystified by her story – whatever it was. I had decided that unlike Beth, I would not be held hostage by the spirit world.

I went about attending to Gemima's list. The counter was spotless, rental invoices written and committee meetings organised. Just before three in the afternoon, as I was about to make myself a cup of tea, a young man, no older than twenty-one, appeared at the desk. He wore a high-vis vest, an impatient look, and was covered in dust. 'Anja?'

I was taken aback. Was this a threat? A man sent by Mrs Hiegel to break my offending hands?

'From Mum,' he said, shoving a plastic container across the desk.

I pried it open. Inside lay a piece of lemon slice and a note: 'The best lemon slice for the best employee.' An unexpected treat.

'Why aren't you up north for the birthday?' I asked the man.

'Couldn't be arsed,' he said with his back to me as he exited the building.

'Thank you,' I called out.

He raised the back of his hand as he disappeared from view.

I held the Tupperware aloft and angled it around. Flecks of coconut slid from atop the icing. I took out the slice and held it between my fingers, appraising it as one would a fine watch. The biscuit base appeared crumbly and buttery, and the icing generous. I put it under my nostrils and breathed deep: citrus, sugar, a hint of almond.

Gemima was suddenly in the room, eating her Twisties and calling me 'love' and 'possum'. She had succeeded in inserting herself in my day-to-day – in her son's too – even while thousands of kilometres away. I could smell her fear of redundancy in this insurance that her time off meant no reprieve for us. For her son, the delivery was a task he'd surely rather not have bothered with – perhaps it was punishment for missing the birthday. For me, it was a treat – a reward for 'keeping them honest'. It was also a reminder: on her return, she would expect her market under control, her list executed and a complimentary verdict on her lemon slice.

My relationship with Lawrence had been one of pragmatism and polite hostility; I was determined, then, to make my relationship with my new boss one of trust and admiration. There was only one way to truly exhibit my loyalty.

I entered the café and ordered a lemon slice from Clara.

'Good to see you eating,' the naive woman said. 'I'll add an extra side of cream for you.'

I brewed myself a tea and sat back at my desk, placing the two slices side by side. Gemima's had a more ample crust and Clara's an excess of frosting. I bit into one and then the other. One was zesty, the other creamy. One had a firm, almond-flake base, the other's was buttery, soft and crumbly. I smelt, I licked, I nibbled, and I rolled frosting around in my mouth till it was nothing but sugar remnants rotting the remaining teeth.

Yes, Gemima's was different to Clara's, but neither one was the better. In fact, I had no preference. If someone had said, 'I want a zesty slice', I would have suggested Clara's, and if someone had asked me to recommend a creamier treat, it would have been Gemima's. But for the life of me, I couldn't pick one. And in truth, I didn't give a flying fuck about the slices or Gemima or her goddamn trip up north, and I resented that she had made her son stop work to bring me this manipulative titbit! Both he and I could manage in her absence.

I tore up her note and wiped all remaining crumbs onto the floor. I took the dollop of cream provided by Clara and shoved the whole thing into my mouth. I then wrote a letter, printed it, stapled it to everyone's invoices and placed it in their pigeonholes.

Dear Colleagues,

Attached to your monthly invoice is a copy of the summary findings from my thesis, 'Distilling Antiques: The Classification of Objects through Essence and Archetype', which was completed as part of my Sotheby's graduate coursework. Why, you ask, have I included this information? After immersing myself in antiquing for the past ten years, I have come to realise that there is a disconnect between customer and dealer – or, rather, that which the customer truly seeks is never found. Antique markets trade in nostalgia: echoes of memory, surpassing one's lost childhood and buried parents, that travel deep into the belly of what Jung described as the 'collective unconscious'. When one walks through our doors one is not only in search of an object, but also of a missing piece of self – something to fill the hole. I believe the market can evolve to meet these primal wants. Say 'yes' to change. Intrigued? If you have questions, I'll be at the front desk until close of business today.

The afternoon passed quickly. Despite an apparent lack of interest in my ideas for change, I was in a cheery mood – perhaps attributable to painkillers prescribed by my doctor.

After tidying the front desk, I made my way to Colin's barn. It was right at the end of the row, about a two-minute walk from the coolstore. I'd been there briefly to drop off Gemima's emergency procedures sheet but had never stepped further in than a couple of feet, let alone bothered to look around. Naval memorabilia held no fascination for me, and while I knew it was attached to the history of my house, I'd been avoiding what had come before. And though I had promised myself I'd abandon the mystical, I couldn't help but feel moved by Colin's persistence. Perhaps he was as lonely as I was. I would listen to the old man's mumbo jumbo, let him feel heard and then be gone.

The door to his barn had a 'Back in Five Minutes' sign displayed. The wind had picked up, blowing fiercely against

my face and making for a rather unpleasant wait, so I took out
the skeleton key and let myself in.

The room was dark, musty; I couldn't tell if the smell came
from Colin's lingering scent or the memorabilia. I ran my hands
over the items on the shelves, collecting dust on my fingertips.
On display were old caps, rope, a giant bell, photos of sailors
sweeping the deck of a ship, and a brown-leather collar and
harness that was large, thick and aged. There were three metal
loops, each as big as my hand, attached to the device: one to
the collar for a leash, and two either side of the harness for
what I could only imagine was tying a dog down to the deck,
perhaps to contain it during a storm.

With my undamaged hand I held the collar up to my neck.
This had been a beast of a dog! I slid the contraption over my
head to judge its girth. The collar sat heavy on my shoulders,
the harness sliding down to my breasts.

The bell above the door rang, and Colin walked in holding
my letter and summary findings. He didn't seem surprised
to see me, or to see me in naval BDSM. 'Weighing up the
evidence?' he said.

'Evidence?'

He gestured to the mirror.

Colin was kinkier than I had imagined. There was a thin
body-length mirror next to the old uniforms. A half-naked
mannequin, missing an arm, beckoned me forward. As I stood
in front of the mirror, I straightened the harness and collar,
examining my body in bondage before my eyes fell to the
leather breastplate.

Burned into the strap was 'ANABA'. My heart raced; the
leather seemed to tighten. I yanked at the harness with both

hands, pulling on my stitches and wincing in pain. 'Get it off!'

Colin rushed to my side and lifted the bonds above my head. '*Easy* does it,' he said, as if I were a bucking horse.

I thanked him, feeble, holding my hand tight in its partner.

He placed the harness back on the shelf and adjusted it so the bold lettering stared out at me.

'Anaba was a dog?'

'Not canine,' Colin said, '*feline.*'

He rounded the corner and retrieved a framed black-and-white photo. In ink, at the bottom corner, was the year 1943. Five men were crouching down in the photo, younger than myself, with sensible haircuts, polished uniforms, big smiles and wide eyes. They were staring at the lens as though it were their future and all that lay ahead was opportunity. Lying down amid the men was a mountain lion. She was smaller than I imagined a cougar to be. Impossibly fluffy, with ticked markings above the eyes, and a dark muzzle. Her throat and chest were lightly fleeced, perhaps white, and her tail curled around the length of her body. Her ears stood straight and faced the camera, but her eyes saw directly through it. She was wearing the collar and harness that I had only minutes ago been modelling. The lettering was bolder in the photo. Three of the men held on to metal chains that attached to the device.

'She was a wartime mascot,' Colin said, 'brought across the Pacific on the USS *Amendment* when they were stationed at HMAS *Hydra*.'

'Anaba,' I said aloud, letting it sink in. My shoulders felt heavy, as though the collar was still in place.

'The name is Native American,' he continued. 'It means "she who returns from war".'

'But she didn't return,' I said under my breath.

He smiled. 'Well, that depends on whom you ask. Locals love to say that she was released into the reserve; there have always been reports of sightings, and she's blamed whenever any livestock turn up dead. There was even that crash last month! A young gentleman drove his car into a pole, inculpating her.' Colin tapped the photo. 'She's the town's favourite scapegoat. Blame Anaba and no one can disprove you.'

I felt the harness constricting my throat, and I scratched at my neck – nothing there.

Colin continued talking. 'Those in the Everglades call them "mountain screamers" because their cry is so ghastly. Only big cat in the world to emit such a noise. Apparently sounds like a woman being murdered.'

He spoke of reports and investigations, detectives and dead dogs. I didn't want to hear it. I needed him to stop. I thought of the shit, smelt the shit, held the bloody rabbit in my arms. Everything was blurring, and then I fell to the ground.

16

I 'd been sent home. Colin had taken one look at me passed out and mangled on the floor and informed the other stallholders. They all agreed: I needed some time off. Even Clara waved me out the door after bestowing her frozen lasagne. I tried to argue, paced and gesticulated, illustrated I was fit and well. I mentioned that Gemima was relying on me, had only hired me to ensure her bidding was done while she vacationed – I couldn't fail on my second day! But my colleagues were hearing none of it. Josh took charge of my exit, said there was no need to inform Gemima – she'd find out soon enough – and in the interim the stallholders could take turns at reception.

'When can I return?'

'When you're ready,' Josh said, which wasn't really an answer considering I was already ready!

I spent the next five days at home, in the quiet, reading on the verandah and tending to Hydra. The November warmth was rewarding her plants, which had grown a foot and were beginning to sprout fruit. The leafy greens were flourishing too. It wouldn't be long before I had enough for a one-person salad.

If my days were quiet, my nights were far from. Anaba …

Anaba … Each night she'd meet me in dreamland and walk alongside me as I stalked the perimeter. Other nights she'd lie in the sun, basking her belly, as I fed live mice to Hydra, who snatched the critters from me with barbed vines. Sometimes Anaba would come to me, her mouth covered in fresh gore. I'd wipe the remains lovingly from her lips.

That morning was warm and bright, and I was spraying pesticide on the veggie garden when my mobile rang on the verandah, startling me – it was a rare breath of reception. Once the phone had been glued to me in anticipation of a call regarding an Eames or a Jacobsen; I had all but abandoned my attachment to it, especially at home with its infrequent 4G. When was the last time it had rung? And who would call me anyway? Perhaps Josh, asking me to return? I felt reluctant to answer, but as I didn't recognise the number, I picked up.

'Anja, it is me, Edmund.'

I was stunned. It had been nearly two years since the funeral, since I had last seen both parents.

'I am in Melbourne,' he said. 'Perhaps you could return the favour?'

'Favour?'

'The hospitality. I have accommodation but thought you could take me out to lunch. I have an entire day to myself so it could also be dinner.'

'I see …'

'I am staying in the city, so somewhere nearby would suit.'

'Um. I'm afraid I no longer live in town.'

'Oh, that is a shame. Another time, then —'

'It's not far! Only an hour, really. I can pick you up from the train station and drop you back later in the day?'

He took his time mulling over the idea. 'Okay … I guess I can afford an adventure.'

I gave him the train details and agreed to meet him at the station. Then I set about cleaning the house to a degree that I thought he'd find respectable. The house was manageable, but the land was not. How was I to explain a mountain lion in the backyard? Hopefully she'd remain hidden. It would be just my luck for her to materialise and tear my father to pieces.

Edmund was one of five passengers to disembark the train. He was as tall and slender as I remembered and wore a backpack slung over his shoulder with polished hiking boots, a pea-green polo shirt and khaki pants. He looked the epitome of a European tourist.

He waved his arm in the air then pulled it down, looking aghast as he neared me. I'd forgotten how alarming my chipped tooth and battered hand were. He said nothing. We kissed both cheeks. I smelt the frangipani and cotton of his aftershave; it was as though he'd just stepped out of the shower and donned freshly laundered clothes. I realised that I hadn't showered, and my hands and bandage were covered in soil from the garden. I hid them behind my back. His hands were neatly manicured, and leather bracelets dangled from his tanned arms.

He caught me admiring the jewellery. 'Botswana. I volunteered at an orphanage there in the 90s.'

We stood on the platform, silent for the longest time. When the train started to move, I remembered why I was there. 'This way,' I said, leading him into the carpark. 'I thought we could go to a winery. The area is known for its —'

'I do not drink – not anymore – not for at least a decade.'

'Oh, a café then?'

'You did not cook?'

'No.'

'Alright ... but modest, I am on a budget. Lina told me to keep it under fifty dollars a day, and I have already spent thirteen dollars on breakfast and seven dollars fifty on my travel here.'

I remembered his house in Copenhagen, its high ceilings and grand archways. 'Do you still own that house in Denmark where I stayed?'

'Oh yes, the family home. We have tenanted it since being in Alice. Good lodgers, always pay their rent on time.'

The budget was a farce, a way for Lina to control him even when he was out of sight. He liked to be controlled, I decided, just as he had been by his parents when they'd demanded he return to Denmark without me.

'I know a bistro that does shared dishes,' I said.

'If it's cheap, I'll eat a lot. Perhaps then I will not need dinner.'

We sat opposite each other at a table in the bistro's garden. I leant back in my chair and opened my chest to the sun before I ordered a rosé and he a glass of lemonade. *He would be fuckable*, I thought – *if, of course, he weren't my father*. I enjoyed his height and smooth brown skin, and he was only nineteen years my senior; I decided it wouldn't be out of the realm of possibility. I sipped my wine and wondered if he had assessed me from this angle. We were both, after all, mostly strangers.

I gave him a wide toothy smile. 'What brings you to Melbourne?'

'It is my birthday. I am fifty! Can you believe it?'

I didn't know if the question was rhetorical, but his lemonade was poised at his lips as if he was waiting for my answer.

'Today?'

'Yes! Lina and I were supposed to visit Melbourne together, but at the last minute there was an emergency in the centre – a bus crash, lots of children hurt.'

'I think I heard something on the radio.'

'Anyway, Lina was forced to stay behind but insisted I come down and enjoy myself. Though we did make sure to downgrade my room and cancel our dinner reservation.'

'Happy birthday!' I said, raising my glass.

'Thank you.' He appeared quite pleased with himself.

Our meal arrived: ricotta gnocchi in pesto sauce, heirloom tomato salad and lamb backstrap.

'It is a funny story,' he said, pushing strips of lamb into his mouth, 'how Lina and I met. Did I ever tell it to you?'

I shook my head.

'We were volunteering together at the co-op. I had seen her around a few times but had not struck up the courage to speak to her. Then one day, she twisted her ankle. She was carrying boxes downstairs and fell. Anyway, she was hobbling around, and I told her to let me have a look at the sprain; my friend was a physio and had taught me a few things. So she agreed, and we sat down in the storeroom and she listened to me talk about torn ligaments and icing procedures, and then when I asked her what she did outside of the co-op, she told me she was a doctor – a paediatrician! She had just let me prattle on and on as if I knew what I was talking about. Funny, ha?'

'How did you meet Mum?'

He seemed shocked, as if I'd mentioned an unspeakable. But what did he expect? I was the product of something, of someone. In fact, I was the very essence of that which he wanted to avoid.

'It was a bar, I think. I cannot remember which one. It was so very long ago.'

I ordered another glass of wine.

'Should you have another one? You still have to drive me back to the station.'

'It's two glasses, Edmund.'

We ate the remainder of the meal in silence.

When the plates were cleared, he asked, 'So, why did you move to the peninsula? I never got to ask at the funeral what you do for work. I remember you were interning at Chiswicks when you rang and left a message.'

It stung to hear him acknowledge the call that he had never returned. 'I'm in antiques. Specialise in mid-century design.'

'I'll never understand how people can spend thousands upon thousands on art and furniture – houses even – yet they cannot spare a dollar to help their fellow man.'

I took a gulp of wine. 'Who are these people you talk of?'

'People! Everyone! The work we do up in Alice is very important. More Australians should be up there helping. It should be a national duty. Conscription!'

'Does Denmark have any social issues?'

'Huge immigration problems. The world is changing. I'm relieved that Lina and I are raising conscientious children. They always ask if their meat had a good life, and whenever they think an injustice has been done, they cry for days! Sometimes they do get overemotional, but that is only as they have big hearts. I'm so proud of them.' He smiled into the distance. 'They speak three languages *and* are learning Warlpiri.'

'Do you want to see where I live?' I said. 'I'm growing a vegetable garden, living sustainably.'

'… Is it far?'

'We have hours,' I said, throwing back my wine.

I drove Edmund down my long, dark, canopied drive. He was fidgeting and clutching at his seatbelt. 'Certainly is far,' he said, rolling down the window.

Perhaps it had occurred to him that I was a stranger, and while we had shared a handful of meals and half my DNA, he knew nothing about me. I hadn't told him about my failed marriage, failed job, or poor judgement calls. He was driving into the depths of the bush with a potential madwoman, no doubt hoping she didn't hold a grudge. I imagined too that he hadn't told Lina about his little trip to visit his firstborn. In fact, I'd have wagered there was no one in the world who knew where he was at that very moment.

When we arrived at the clearing he let go of his seatbelt and dropped his shoulders. What was it that relaxed him so? Knowing there was an out, a cliff from which to jump? I parked the car and he got out gingerly, as if expecting to be sprung. I moved towards the house, but he wasn't following; he was walking towards the water – I'd forgotten how captivating the view was. 'There is a ship out there,' he said.

'It's grounded. Has been left to rot since the 80s. A lot of red tape, apparently.' I stood next to him. 'The local government want to maintain it as a tourist attraction, the naval base want it as a training ground, others see it as a piece of regional history that should be preserved.'

'But either way,' he said, 'it is wasting away in purgatory. Neither this, nor that. A vessel of other people's ideas.'

He looked incredibly sad, and I wondered if he saw himself in that ship. I wondered if we all did.

'Where is your husband, Anja?' he said, turning sharply towards me and refocusing his attention.

'Gone.' I shrugged.

'That man holding the wreath at your mother's funeral?'

'Yes.'

'What happened?'

'… I think, perhaps, that neither of us could live up to the expectations assigned by the other. It was an expectation of familiarity, an initial promise made – that you'll be one person entirely for the rest of your days – that didn't really hold up. It's ridiculous, of course, to expect so much of someone, but we'd known each other from schooldays, and because of that remained children – despite the marriage and house and dinner parties – our personalities fixed, predetermined … And then when Mum died, I needed more than he could offer, more than any human could.'

Edmund said nothing, returning his attention to the ship. I felt free speaking to him, divulging, as if those things for so long unsaid could now see light. Was this bonding?

'I didn't help the situation,' I continued. 'I knew, for a long time, that I was lying. Afraid to be alone, I tethered him to my side, lulled him with promises I couldn't keep. I guess combining our lives so young didn't prepare me so well for adult responsibility.' I laughed quietly.

'Yes, but you are not that young,' Edmund said. 'Surely you know by now how to navigate maturity?'

The rebuke stung. 'Well, I'm not *nineteen*, if that's what you mean,' I said with a sneer.

'Exactly! You are an adult. You know what deception and entrapment are, and you committed them anyway.' He turned from the ocean, from me, and walked towards Hydra, then bent down to tug at the weeds nesting alongside her hull. 'It is about responsibility,' he said.

I stormed after him. 'And that's what you're an expert in, responsibility?'

The afternoon air was muggy, and my underarms began to tingle and sweat.

'Yes,' he said, ceasing his weed pulling and staring at the veggie patch. 'It is a principle I try to adhere to in my life.'

'Oh, I forgot, such a moral man, responsible for all the world's children!'

He stood up and came towards me. 'No, Anja,' he said, 'I am responsible because when I was younger – just a teenager – someone was not responsible with me. She took no responsibility for looking after me!' He pounded his chest. 'Yes, okay, I liked the sex, what young boy does not. And if we had not had a child, I would have said that I did, in a way, love her. But you have stained all memories I have of that relationship. You are the biggest regret of my life, not because I want to be cruel, or because I think you are a bad person, or even that you make me feel like a failed father. It is because I was a teenager, and she wanted a child.'

I hated the word 'she' as it sashayed off his tongue. 'Use her name,' I said.

'What?' He leant in, unable to hear me above the wind, which had picked up and was blowing from across the ocean.

'Use her name.'

His insistence on a pronoun had whipped and snarled, a reminder that only I held the key to who she was. His skewed vision was tarnishing a whole memory. She had enjoyed chess, Chinoiserie and sewing names onto clothes. She would laugh when a lift was full of people, finding it impossible to remain quiet. She ordered her silk pyjamas from Italy and greeted everyone she passed on the street. She cried easily and was hard to anger. Took her coffee with milk and sugar. When she died, it was in silence – the cancer stripping her throat, thrush invading her mouth. Perhaps that was what had drawn me to the squid: they had also perished in silence. They too deserved to have a witness, someone to testify that they had existed upon the earth. That there was memory of them and of her.

'I'm sorry, Anja. I should not have come. What she —'

'Maggie!'

'What Maggie was to me and what Maggie is to you can never be reconciled. It was a mistake to try this out. Please take me back to the station.'

'Fucking hitchhike!'

He nodded. 'Goodbye, Anja … and … and you really should have that tooth fixed.'

He walked off towards the dark of the canopied driveway, Mr Responsibility, crowned in moralism. The overhanging trees blew fiercely in the wind. Did I have a duty to make sure he reached the road? What if Anaba snared him in her jaws, tearing and gnashing her way through tasty righteous innards?

But I should let him go! Let him fend for himself for once – no Lina, no parents.

I thought of Mrs Hiegel leaning back into a chair no longer there, that second of humiliation upon her face before she broke her coccyx. If I relinquished Edmund to the bush, knowing he might not emerge, was that poor judgement? Did I have a responsibility to his children, to all the children he burdened with principles?

'Wait!' I called out after him. 'Let me drive you.'

We sat in silence the whole drive there. At the station, he thanked me. 'Quite the fiftieth,' he said. 'I feel I have come full circle.'

I gave him a half smile and shook his hand, knowing full well we would never meet again.

I watched from the car as he boarded the train. Heavy rain clouds burst and fat drops fell upon the windscreen. I couldn't help but think of his full circle. How I envied him that sense of closure: not on our relationship, which had indeed rounded all four corners, but on his life, where everything had returned to the beginning. But where was my beginning? Fleeting childhood homes with my mother? School with Beth and Hayden? Or was it within the old creaking halls of Geoffrey Browne that I'd find my resolution?

[ITEM 14]
17:00, 15 September 1985.
Interview — Commanding Officer's Headquarters:
Lieutenant Brendan Quartermain & Captain Glen
Morrissey

GM: Christ this storm! Have you got everything you
need in the cottage? Firewood? Extra blankets?
Be sure to pull the shutters tight. Greatest
storm in sixty-four years, they're saying! Have
you seen the ships swaying in the inlet? They
think that grounded ship is going to sink! Good
riddance, I say, as long as it doesn't break
up and find its way to shore — bureaucratic
nightmare!

You'll forgive me if I haven't got long. As you
can tell, we're chasing our arses with repairs.
Generators down and flooding in the mess halls.
I've never seen anything quite like it.

Cyclone Dolly, they're calling her. Once had
a girlfriend called Dolly, when I was in high
school. At times, I think she was the love of my
life. I remember running ten kilometres after
football practice to her house, just to tell
her I loved her. I could barely get the words
out; it was the first time I'd ever said those
words to anyone other than my mother. She left
me, Dolly, for some rich kid at university. It
was my fault, though: she caught me with some
neighbourhood gal — whose name I can't even
remember — well, that's a lie, I do remember,
but it's just so unimportant. I was young, an
idiot, but I never forgot her — Dolly, that is.
When she caught us in the act she took off her
high heel to smack me, like something out of a
cartoon or what you may imagine an old lady to

205

do to a dog. It would have been funny if she hadn't been crying so much. Sometimes at night, when my wife is away visiting her sister or our kids, I'll open a shoebox that I store memories in. I like to look at this one old photo of Dolly and me in a pool hall. I'm in a leather jacket thinking I'm Brando from *The Wild One*, and she's in this little cardigan, her long straight hair, shiny and auburn, down to her bum. Of course, you can't see the hair colour in the photo, but I remember running my fingers through it like it was yesterday. Anyway, now a Dolly has come to torment me again, so you'll forgive me, Lieutenant, if I don't have much time to chat.

BQ: We can keep it brief. You said that if my investigation was to come back in your direction then you would sit down with me.

And all roads lead to me?

Perhaps a side street. I believe Mr Crawley presented his environmental concerns to you and a few other leading officers at a meeting earlier in the year?

<u>Christ!</u> You've been speaking to him? He's nothing but a conspiracist, believes there's a big cat prowling the property. I may work for the government, but I can smell bullshit when I hear it. I'm hoping to get rid of that nature reserve — it's too much work, waste of resources, would make a great football field and park. That's what I told Mr Crawley!

So you don't believe him?

Believe him? Every rural town in the country has a big cat story. And that's all they are — stories!

And the lair?

Have you seen the so-called lair?

I'm hoping to, when the rain stops.

Well, good luck with that. It's nothing but ash and charcoal.

Burned?

Like the inside of an oven — by Crawley himself. Claimed his blackberry poison exploded and 'poof', no more evidence.

… Captain, I must admit, I feel I'm going in circles. What was described as a theft and animal slayings by subversives is looking more and more likely to be a series of coincidences, with no break-in, and most likely the work of a voracious feral fox. Perhaps this is a job better suited for the wildlife authority?

Lieutenant, I couldn't say it better myself. If it were up to me, you'd never have been asked here. If you'd like to wrap up your report, I'd be happy to cast my eye over it. Join us tonight in the Captain's Dining Room? Let's keep the dead buried and those rumours quashed.

Rumours, Captain? You're aware of more people who believe there's a big cat on base?

Look, Lieutenant, people latch on to things, superstitions and whatnot. It's not the kind of thing we need to be looking into. Especially with the British in town!

Captain, I was assigned here to investigate all leads, regardless of how absurd they seem. What rumours?

[Exhales deeply] … There's a story from the 40s, during wartime. A visiting US mascot. Mountain lion, I believe, with some kind of American Indian name. It's an urban legend now — the whole town's heard of it. But that doesn't make it real, Lieutenant.

What happened to the mascot?

Not quite sure myself. Went back home, I imagine, or with the boys to the front. Not the best mascot if you ask me — can't exactly let a lion roam the ship alone. Ever heard of Nils Olav? Now that's a mascot! King penguin. Head of the Norwegian Armed Forces.

Why didn't you mention this before?

The animal didn't stay here! And even if she did, she'd be over forty years old now. I don't think cats can live that long, do you?
    And that's my time up, Lieutenant. Perhaps life does come full circle, hey, and that's why Dolly is here to whip my arse again.

Now excuse me, Officer, I have a date with a
thunderstorm.

[ITEM 15]
20:00, 15 September 1985.
Recording: Two-way Transmitter between Base &
Cottage.

[inaudible] Come … Lieute … Over … It's … lin
Tatter … I have something … to see. Over.

This is Quarte … The storm … ting the transmit
… Over.

Can … meet … Archives … nant? Over.

Archives? … there … twent … Out.

17

The wind was furious as I drove back to the property, and my windscreen wipers beat angry and in vain against relentless rain. I considered pulling over but decided instead to step on the gas and try for the safety of home. A storm warning sounded on the radio, and a distant siren from HMAS *Hydra* drilled into the air. I pulled up to my farm gate, which was already shaking in its lock. Outside the car, wild wind slapped my face. I could hear the ocean from where I stood, thundering on the shore. I hunched over and opened the gate, pushing against the wind to secure it behind my red-painted rock before jumping back into the car.

But as I drove forward, the rock rolled, releasing the gate so that it crashed against my car, scratching the doors like fingernails on an expensive chalkboard. I jumped out again to survey the damage: both panels gashed. The car and *I*, now vandalised by the land.

Thunder clapped like a shotgun in my ear. I jumped in the car again, leaving the gate, which blew savagely back and forth. I belted myself in and sped down my drive, awaiting death by falling branch. The radio turned to static.

I arrived at the clearing. My house was barely holding

up, the corrugated roof rippling in the gale, threatening to break free. The sea was frothing enough to spray the cliff-side deckchairs, which had blown over. I looked to Hydra: her canvas windbreak had torn from the earth and flown to a far corner of the property. Her plants were uprooting from their soil, her six eyes pleading. I moved my car to protect her – a Renault shield against the ocean and the worst of the gale.

Another smack, a blinding light, and the branches of the moonah I'd parked next to rained down onto the car. I screamed. For whom? The trunk of the tree had been split and was glowing red. Branches lined the bonnet and roof, scratching against the vehicle like the claws of an ancient stick monster. Thankfully none had broken the windscreen or concaved the roof. It was too dangerous to get out, especially with the threat of lightning. *Don't strike the house, don't strike the car*, I repeated to myself. I looked at my phone – no reception. I tuned the radio, flicking the dial – nothing.

The ocean was angry, alive and sizzled with lightning bolts across the horizon. In the distance, five bolts struck the water, thundering down in unison. The grounded ship was swaying, ascending like Poseidon from the waves and smacking her stern as the water dropped beneath her. She was crazy, wild, surely would not survive, and then – a bolt of lightning into her stern, another her bow. She split, black smoke rising into the air. I could hear her cracking even through the storm, like the bones of an old woman rising from a chair. The ocean hissed and howled until it claimed her and she had sunk below. The sky then grew dark except for flashes of light across the ocean. I curled up in the back seat, wrapped myself in a picnic rug and fell asleep.

I was haunted that night by macabre tick insects. They ran the length of my throat and back. I'd swipe at the buggers, but they were ceaseless like the tide. They wanted to mate with each other, to merge their bodies on mine. They locked mouths, limbs and sex organs, joining together like a puzzle. I scratched at them, but their shells were of leather. I rolled in the dirt, trying to shake the beasts, but that only compressed their scutum, forging a shield, a second skin, onto my own that looped my throat, cradled my back and pulsed with their bodily rhythm. The faster they vibrated the tighter the armour became until I was forced upright, spine straight, shoulders back, chest forward like a tin solider. I was then a little too convex, my neck a little too constricted. My shoulders rounded their blades and slipped their sockets. My rib cage buckled and tore through skin, flaying my chest that, in tsunami motion, stripped the skin from my entire body. My legs and arms bent backwards, my head nestled into my spine. I'd become the armour: a rounded bloody ball protecting the mating parasites.

I awoke gasping for air. The sun was well into the sky, and the car windows were steamed from my breath. Outside was calm, not a swaying branch to be seen. The radio crackled on, the announcer speaking with apprehension, disbelief and uncertainty; I too was uncertain of the words I was hearing. Was I still dreaming? I crawled into the front seat and turned up the volume. A lunatic was winning the US presidential election. Any remnants of trust I once had in a universal order dissolved before me. I turned off the radio and pushed open the car door, fighting against branches.

Boughs and limbs littered the land, more having fallen during the night. The moonah that had been struck by lightning shone with charcoals like a pizza oven. The railing of my verandah had snapped off, and a window facing the ocean had blown, but other than that the house remained intact, albeit a little beaten.

I went behind my car. Beneath some loose branches and twigs, Hydra was undamaged, her plants remaining rooted and her six eyes thankful.

I walked to the edge of the cliff. The ocean was without a ripple, and for a moment I nearly panicked, thinking I was in a silent eye of the storm, before reminding myself that it had been hours and she had surely passed. The grounded cargo ship was gone too and with her any battle for ownership.

Something caught my eye, glistening in the water below. Pirate treasure? It was small, barely visible and not far from the shore. In the sober light of day, the route down and back seemed less troublesome, even with a bandaged hand. I shifted my body over the rocks and waded into the ocean barefoot. The water was warm. I rolled my jeans, walked in up to my calves and bent down. The glistening object was made from bronze and silver; it was as long as my hand with a thin tube attached to a small bulb. Drug paraphernalia? An elf's tobacco pipe? The whiplash design was indicative of the Art Nouveau period, and melded to the bulb was a bronze image of an anchor. I am not traditionally an admirer of excessive design epochs, though the piece was undoubtedly charming. Had it sunk with the grounded ship? I pocketed the object and turned around.

Crouched on a boulder, with a flailing fish between her jaws, was Anaba. She appeared smaller in the flesh than in the photo and was fawn in colour, her hunched shoulders as solid as the rock she graced. Her green eyes locked onto mine, her ears shot back and whiskers flared. She clenched tight her yellow fangs, and the fish went limp. She was majestic and beguiling and corporeal. A growl vibrated from her throat.

I stepped towards her and she fled, bounding from rock to rock and into the reserve – gone in seconds, as if she had never been. But she had been there. *She was here*, I told myself. *She did, for a moment, exist with me on this beach, under this same sky, breathing this same air.*

18

Cougars and Cougar Safety 101

Be careful walking alone in any national park. Never run or walk with music in your ears. It is also recommended that women on their period refrain from hiking alone; some believe cougars are attracted to the scent of menstrual blood, although this is yet to be proven. When camping in or living near a national park, be sure to lock pets inside at night and do not leave out any food.

If you do happen to spot a cougar, raise your hands and make noise. Do not turn your back on the cougar. They are ambush predators. Do not run. These actions will trigger the animal's hunting drive. Walk backwards slowly until the cougar is long out of sight.

The male cougar can reach 220 pounds, though females are much smaller. They can leap fifteen feet in the air and reach speeds of fifty miles per hour. Their scream has been described as that of a tortured woman. Nocturnal and crepuscular, they are the biggest cat to purr and are also known to emit a bird-like chirp. To muffle their footsteps, their claws retract like those of a house cat, and their jaws have the strength to break the neck of any deer. Once a kill is made, the cougar disembowels its prey before dragging the carcass to a secluded location. They will make a large kill every ten days, though can survive too off regularly consuming smaller animals. Similar to other carnivores they like to live in caves or other shelters, and they cover their kills with dirt and twigs. The cougar is adept at living in any landscape, from barren deserts to high mountain peaks; they have also been spotted in Canadian coastal villages. Without predators, the cougar can live for twenty years.

Puma concolour is their binomial name, though they go by many others: mountain lion, panther, catamount, tawny tiger, mountain screamer, shadow cat, ghost cat.

Cougars are solitary animals, which makes them difficult to study and understand. If you see a cougar, that is only because it wants to be seen.

With no access to the work computer, I returned to the local library in order to gather the above information, which I sourced from an *Encyclopedia Britannica* (1994), a hand guide to Californian trekking routes (1972), and a book on North American flora and fauna (2003). One should always arm oneself with knowledge, especially when cohabitating with an apex predator.

As informative as my excursion was, it didn't answer my main question: why had I stepped towards Anaba? I had walked unflinching and unthinking into her path. Was it the same reason I'd carted myself down the rocks and into the ocean while intoxicated, or why I'd stood on Hill Pass in the dark, drunk and driven by sex? It would have been easy to blame it on my propensity for flirtation with annihilation, but this felt … 'deeper', more profound than a death drive.

Anaba was pure id and pure beauty, without herself knowing what beauty was. Perhaps she was the Prima I'd been chasing, unknowingly, my entire life. Something of immeasurable value, rarity and allure. The ultimate Prima – the cat's meow! – in a lifetime of hunting.

And what department would she inhabit? With her primal wail, unmatched strength and life in the shadows, she spoke of a forgotten time, of a primitive soul. The Department of Ancient Self?

Since our encounter, my heart had beaten to a different rhythm. Facing down a lion one feels at once alive and insignificant. A gaiety had sprung in my step, one founded on nearly losing myself to her, to the wild. She was in my psyche now, like a drug I couldn't kick and didn't want to. I needed to see her again.

As I left the library, my mobile rang.

'Hello?' I said to the unknown number.

'Is this Anja Harley?' a woman asked me.

'Speaking.'

'This is Sam from Telecommunications. I'm happy to inform you that an internet connection is now available for your property.'

'Someone died?' I said.

There was a sigh. I realised instantly that she was the woman I'd spoken to over a month ago.

'The line,' the woman continued, 'was relinquished and —'

'Because someone died?'

There was silence and then, 'Yes, Ms Harley, someone died. And since your house is next on the waitlist, the connection is yours. Would you like me to find out some details of the death?'

'No. Your honesty is sufficient.'

She was silent for a moment. 'We can send someone this week. You don't have to be there.'

'Perfect,' I said and hung up.

That night, after chopping my verandah rail into firewood and boarding up my blown window, I took from the freezer two of Hydra's mice. Both black-and-white creatures, they could have been siblings. Without a hint of live flesh, they seemed unappetising, so I placed them in a bowl and put them in the microwave for thirty seconds; the kitchen smelt ripe with mildew. I placed the bowl under the verandah and turned off the light. I then snuggled into my leather sofa and awaited my kitty cat.

I kept vigil all night, but she never came.

After sunrise I walked onto the verandah. The bowl was covered in ants and had drawn the attention of a menacing wasp. I poured water on the dish until the ants drowned and the wasp retreated. The mice were hollowed. I flung their bodies onto Hydra.

The next night I defrosted two more mice, and the next and the next, but Anaba never showed. Nor was there any sign she'd been lurking in the shadows – no tracks, scat or dead wildlife.

On the fifth day, I received a text message from Gemima. *Back from holiday. I think you'd better come in. Don't you?*

[ITEM 16]
20:45, 15 September 1985.
Interview—Archives: Lieutenant Brendan Quartermain
& Professor Colin Tatterson

CT: [inaudible] Lieutenant, quick! Come in.

BQ: Thank you. Sorry it took so long, I had to pull over and …

Here, let me hang your jacket … Lieutenant, you're pale … Are you all right?

Oh, yes … fine, fine … Thank you.

Some tea to calm those storm nerves?

Do you have anything stronger? It's, um, it's been a wild night.

It certainly has, Lieutenant. [cupboards opening and closing] Thankfully there's no storm damage to this building, but just looking out the window I can see tomorrow's clean-up will be a task. Was there any damage incurred out there in the Wild West? [drink being poured] … Lieutenant?

Ah, no. No. A few trees down, but the shack has held.

Good to hear. There you go, Seppelt port. It's all I have, I'm afraid. I keep it in the cupboard for the local Rotary Club. They rent out the building twice a year when going over their budget, always leave a mess.

Thank you.

Listen to that wind howl! … So, Lieutenant …

So …

… So, I asked you here as I've found something that you may find rather exciting. I heard around town that you were speaking to Mr Crawley, and I thought perhaps I'd better find you some counterevidence before your mind travelled too far down the more enticing path.

Counter? You too know about the lion?

Everybody knows about the mountain lion, but the creature lived <u>forty years ago</u>. The Australian landscape is prime for this sort of rumour and mythology. We have no real predators, so we invent ones. Perhaps deep down we know it's not our land, it's alien. That's why the threat is something that cannot truly exist. The threat itself is foreign, just as we are. And anyway, you're not hunting a big cat — you're hunting a man. A man who thinks he can use this creature for his own ends. As you may have realised, Lieutenant, I take a rather moral stance with regards to this cat. I feel for any being that is caged and exploited.

[sighs] What is it you wanted to show me?

After you left yesterday, I began to think about Anaba. More precisely, what happened to her. We have documented proof of her arrival with the USS *AMENDMENT*: photos, customs reports. I hadn't, however, seen any documentation pertaining to her departure from our shores. It's an interesting line of inquiry, as the Americans burned most of their documents before they left. We may have been their allies, but they still didn't want us monitoring their administration or viewing any codes they had used. We mustn't kid ourselves — behind the scenes, both countries were gathering intel on each other.

Anyway, what they couldn't destroy were our documents concerning the land. After you left I did some digging, and I found a map of the base from the 40s. It shows that where our shooting range now lies was once landfill and a garbage-processing plant. So, I went over the utilities documents from that period, and there — among instructions on human waste management and information on the burning of plastics — was a document stamped for approval by HMAS ███████ regarding the burial of a US mascot. Take a look.*

[paper rustling] … So, the medal is hers!

Lieutenant, you're missing the point: she was shot, buried. What more proof do you need?

… It's just … I think … I think I saw something. Tonight, in the storm.

Ah yes, the look of death about you. You're not the first. We often search for answers, explanations in an uncertain world. It seems we would prefer the mysticism to the chaos. I can't speak for what Officer Gibbs saw that night, or what slaughtered Officer Robbins's dog. But I believe in the paper

---

*A note to the reader: Please refer to Item 17 for a copy of the document.

trail. And the paper trail verifies that there are no big cats here — not since 1942, anyway. We may wish for history to repeat itself, but it doesn't always. I do wonder …

Yes.

… Mr Crawley, he has unfettered access to the reserve and knowledge of animal behaviour, and is acutely aware — as we all are — of the looming budget cuts. Would it not be in his interest to wrangle more funding for the wetlands, specifically for pest eradication?

Sounds like you've been conducting your own investigation, Mr Tatterson.

Oh? Well, as I said earlier, I'm just here to provide the rational argument.

… Looks like the rain has stopped. I'd better get back to my lodgings before it starts up again. Thank you for the port.

[ITEM 17]

2 June 1942.

Copy of the document detailing the internment and euthanising of the United States Mascot known as Anaba (mountain lion)

USS *AMENDMENT*: The Destruction and Removal of Mascot VI

As of this morning the Australian Federal Government has moved to prohibit Australian servicemen from travelling overseas and returning home with live animal mascots. This has followed a near outbreak of yellow fever in Western Australia from infected monkeys travelling with a Polish Army unit from Northern Africa. While the prohibition does not restrict American mascots, it has raised concerns over the continued harbouring of Mascot VI, the mountain lion known as Anaba. She has been costly to feed and time-consuming for her handlers, not to mention the difficulties of the passage across the Pacific, which was unpleasant for her and dangerous for our men. The USS *AMENDMENT* is shipping out in July, and Captain Douglas Smith does not want the animal on board.

The idea of releasing her into the wild has been discussed, but the cat's tame nature means that she is likely to wander into nearby farms or find her way back to base. It has thus been ordered that she will be destroyed by a single bullet to the back of the head. As gratitude for her service, and to appease the men who have grown fond of her, she will be awarded the Expeditionary Medal. Traditionally the US Military does not bestow awards on animals, but as there will be no campaign record of the medal,

we are willing to make an exception. HMAS ████
has agreed to dispose of the remains.

19

Gemima was as red as one of the northern crustaceans she'd been sucking back; I doubted if her skin had seen a spot of sunscreen the entire trip. She was applying aloe vera to her neck and chest when I arrived.

'You couldn't possibly believe the time I've had!' she said, discarding the bottle and wiping her hands on her capri pants. 'Every meal, *every meal*, she sits me next to that cousin. And all *she* wants to do is talk about her recent gallbladder operation. And I'm not talking one or two meals – the whole holiday was planned: bushwalks one day, lunch at the marina the next. For my fiftieth all I did was a simple barbie, but no, not for my sister. We had to make a song and dance for her. Oh, and she shouted us – to all of it! Couldn't miss an opportunity to pay for everyone – show off how much money she has. She even wanted to pay for our serviced apartment – can you imagine! But that was simply a step too far. I insisted that we pay. I wouldn't want her thinking we're a charity case.' I opened my mouth to agree, but as I did Gemima let out a wail. 'Ah! It's worse than I thought!' she cried, shuffling me to a nearby stool. 'Open wide.' She guided my head side to side in her hands. 'Josh said it was bad, but *this* ... You look like a nuff nuff.'

My ghastly appearance had worked in my favour.

'You're on painkillers?' she asked.

'I was, for my hand.' I lifted the once-bandaged hand; a pink bandaid covered the dissolving stitches.

'That explains the letter you sent out.'

'Letter?'

'Yes, love, bits of gobbledygook – something about being unconscious and having dead parents. All very dark stuff. I won't be going away again, that's for sure.'

I feigned surprise and amnesia. There was no point in trying to educate Gemima. Under her command, the market would only ever see the world through a limited lens. It was a fight I no longer had in me, so I leant into her sunburnt chest and closed my eyes.

'Let's keep you back of house today, possum,' she said, guiding me behind a partition.

I spent the morning as Gemima had instructed, dutifully out of sight and deep in admin, though with thoughts far from the task at hand. My research into cougars and my tempting treats had failed to manifest Anaba. Had she felt threatened by my actions? Sensed in me a longing that she was fearful to fulfill? I needed to speak to someone who knew the cat.

At lunchtime I walked to the end of the barn row and knocked upon Mu-Sea-Um's open shop door. Colin was at the counter, seemingly absorbed in the *Sea Breeze Leader*, the peninsula's local rag. He looked up at me, and a tear dropped onto the page. 'Oh, Anja, how are you feeling?'

Uncomfortable, was my initial thought. 'I'm sorry,' I said, 'I can come back if this is a bad time.' It wasn't a question; I edged towards the door.

'No, no. Come in. I'm just … lost in memory.' He said the word 'memory' as all elderly people do – knowing their younger listener has no true concept of its meaning.

I looked down at the paper. Below the title 'Resurrected' was a photo of some kind of … bilby.

'Long-toothed bandicoot,' Colin said. 'Ever heard of it?'

I shook my head.

'It was thought to be extinct – twenty years now – but they just found one in the HMAS *Hydra* reserve. Remarkable, isn't it?'

I nodded, not quite sure if a resurrected bilby was worth my tears. 'Colin, I need to talk about Anaba.'

'Yes, I thought as much,' he said, folding the paper.

'I've left out food for four nights now, but she hasn't returned.'

'Returned? Anja, Anaba is *dead*, has been for seventy years.' He ducked behind the counter. I could hear the dial of a combination safe. He retrieved a document and slid it towards me. 'I had planned to show you this before you hit the deck. It's all in here.'

The document was titled *Australia Station Intelligence Report: Naval Intelligence Division*.

'There was an investigation into Anaba, thirty years ago now – slaughtered animals and whatnot.' He sat back on his chair, looking weary. 'At the time I was working as an archivist at the base – you can read my interviews.'

I flicked through the document.

'It's not an original copy,' he said, 'but it holds the vital information, shows a cohesive path.' His eyes were reddening as though he might cry again.

I asked what the report revealed.

He shrugged. 'That she's dead. Was destroyed, shot.'

I too wanted to cry. 'But what about the evidence, these dead animals you mentioned?'

Colin sighed. 'The investigation found that the wetlands' manager, a man by the name of Wayne Crawley, was … framing, for lack of a better word, the dead cat.' Colin then spoke of an inquiry, an unceremonious firing, plans for a football field. 'You have to understand!' he said suddenly. 'There were budget cuts. I was worried for my own department, my own job.'

I knew the feeling.

'I wasn't coerced into anything, and the evidence did point to Crawley, but I do wonder … If I hadn't steered the ship, illuminated the path, would the investigative officer have drawn the same conclusion?' Colin's hands held together, shaking gently. And then, 'He killed himself, Crawley, a year after being stood down.'

I placed my hands on Colin's. Tears ran heavy down his face, and he withdrew from my touch, retrieving a handkerchief to wipe his cheeks. When his face was dry, he took my hands again and held tight. '*Thank you*,' he said.

Anaba had slipped my grip. There was a seventy-year chasm between us. The shadow cat was of the same place but another time, like my mother's image in her dresser mirror. I thought of those who'd blamed Anaba for their own failures: the Commodore driver, this Crawley, me. And for me, it wasn't just Anaba; I'd sunk into a morass of blame-shifting. Perhaps there was more Edmund in me than I cared to recognise.

I told Gemima I was feeling unwell and left work early. I arrived home in the early afternoon to see that the internet had been connected. I retrieved my laptop, which had been collecting dust beneath my bed, hooked up the router and logged on. It had been months since I'd last bothered to check my emails. But there in my empty house, kilometres from any other soul, there was no time like the present to dip back into a life forgone.

One thousand and seventy-six emails. I groaned, poured a glass of red and scrolled to the beginning of the drudgery. My inbox was littered with makeup promotions, offers of cheap flights to Greece, Sotheby's alumni news, and real-estate openings.

On the fifth page my fingers leapt from the keyboard. An invitation! I appeared to still be subscribed to Geoffrey Browne's mailing list. I laughed, thinking of Ian from HR. He truly had overlooked the online system … but then again, perhaps this wasn't an automated email, perhaps someone had clicked 'send'.

The invitation read 'Mid-Century Design, Modern Australian Art: The Joseph Hiegel Collection'. Under this was a photo of Fran. I'd almost forgotten her face – no, that's a lie. I recognised every pore and blemish as though it were my own. She was dressed in a chic black suit, and her hand was resting on Mrs Hiegel's shoulder as the old woman sat, ankles crossed, upon – yes, you guessed it – PP501, my ruinous chair.

Fran was looking triumphant, her face tilted upwards, and for good reason: the caption read 'Specialist Fran O'Brian'. The little vulture had done it. She'd overcome her disastrous dress sense and dubious aesthetic sensibilities to fill my shoes, as though she had morphed into me – or, rather, the person I had planned to be.

Guests were welcomed to the event by a stock photo of two toffed up women, laughing and clinking champagne flutes. And as if timed by astral influence – a stranger's death, secure internet, an off-the-cuff decision to check my inbox – the auction was that evening.

I wrote Davina an email detailing care instructions for Hydra and requesting she find a tenant for the property. Outside, I bent down to kiss my monster's three fanged mouths, then I jumped in the car and sped off down the freeway, towards my coup de grâce.

20

Fran's first mistake as specialist was holding the auction at the Geoffrey Browne premises. Joseph's house, with its wild garden and sophisticated design, would have been the perfect setting for moody twilight bidding, and the furniture had undoubtedly lost some of its magic dust in transit.

For auctions, the house requires that all attendees, whether voyeur or buyer, RSVP. With millions of dollars on display, it's important that everyone who traipses through the front door be registered. For any on-site auction, all pieces are presented in white-painted showrooms, similar to those of a gallery. There is champagne and a speech, usually given by Lawrence, about the history and significance of the collection, and expounding on the evening's Primas. Food is themed – yakitori for Japanese antiquities, devilled eggs for Art Deco design. Estate auction canapés are a fraction less predictable and could be inspired by the deceased's interests or personality. When a famous footballer's memorabilia went under the hammer, I was tickled to discover party pies being served. Because the Joseph Hiegel auction showcased twentieth-century Australian artworks and mid-century pieces, I predicted mini meatballs in the Modernist showroom and kangaroo skewers where the art hung. No one who joined our register would ever have to go hungry.

'Our' – I was still saying that word. Stockholm syndrome.

As I wasn't registered for the auction, I snuck around to the back entrance near the carpark; the security code was unchanged – thank you, Ian! Above the showrooms there's a booth-like space where black-and-white films were once projected. The space was easy enough to break into – I'd brought Hydra's shovel to jimmy it open.

High above the showrooms, I had an unobscured view of the guests and antiques. I felt like the Phantom of the Opera, damaged and vengeful, my broken tooth tingling. I ran my tongue back and forth over its crooked edge. '*Ptu, ptu,*' I whispered into the dark.

The rooms began to fill, and the smell of food wafted up into my booth. I'd guessed correctly: mini meatballs. The waiters were also serving mini fondue cups and bite-size lamingtons. I spotted Bertie; he was dressed in a silk vest and accosting the lamington waiter. After taking three of the treats, he stationed himself under a Norman Lindsay nude, which he spent a great deal of time admiring.

I next spotted Mrs Hiegel in the corner of the room, shielded by Miranda and a large walnut armoire. On the opposite wall was the sideboard I'd catalogued, though now it held the complete Susie Cooper collection. How many weary hours had the lost piece taken to source? Fran was hovering by the set, trying not to appear possessive whenever a potential buyer peeked under a saucer. She wore a 70s-inspired red pantsuit that clung flatteringly to her body.

Next to the sideboard, on a white platform and presented as

it should *always* have been, was my chair: my ruinous, PP501, bedraggled, one-of-a-kind chair.

A glass chimed. It was Lawrence, adorned by a mint-coloured tie and ready for his speech. He was standing at the far wall, opposite PP501. Fran manoeuvred herself to stand by his side as the crowd gathered around them and fell silent.

This was my chance. I crept downstairs into the showroom.

If you see a cougar, it is only because she wants to be seen.

'It's not often,' Lawrence said, 'that we're bestowed such a rare and prestigious collection as this.'

Do not turn your back on a cougar. They are ambush predators.

'Joseph Hiegel,' Lawrence continued, 'was no mere collector: he was a visionary, curating with care and cheek.'

I edged towards my chair, leaning forward to skim the oh-so-familiar smooth Danish oak with my fingertips.

'Tonight's auction will take us on a journey through Scandinavia to Australia.'

I slid the chair's arm into my left palm. Time seemed to stand still, and then —

'It's her!' Mrs Hiegel screamed. 'My *God*, it's *her*!'

If you do happen to spot a cougar, raise your hands and make noise.

The crowd spun around, aghast when they saw the shovel in my right hand.

'*Jesus Christ*,' Lawrence blurted into the microphone.

A man stepped towards me. I held high the shovel as I slipped between the chair and the sideboard of Susie Cooper. He backed off.

'Anja.' Fran was calm, composed. She slunk through the crowd towards me. 'You're acting a bit mad, don't you think?'

I raised the shovel higher.

'This isn't a good look for you,' she said.

'And what is it you know of aesthetics?' I countered.

'You have choices, Anja, you can put down the shovel and —'

'That's where you're wrong, Fran. It's *you* who has been gifted a choice.'

Her head tilted. I knew she was intrigued and enjoying the spotlight.

'The choice,' I said, 'between the Susie Cooper and the Wegner.'

She wavered, looking confused.

I pointed with my shovel. 'An admirable collection of well-crafted china or a pure, refined yet dishevelled chair.'

Fran may have been confused, but Lawrence was not. 'Don't do this, Anja,' he said into the safety of the microphone, not daring to slip from his podium.

'This isn't me,' I said, poking the shovel into the air with each syllable. 'This. Is. Fran. Fran's. Choice.'

The shovel poking had shaken her. 'Um, I don't, I don't understand.'

'I'm asking you to choose,' I said. 'Which item do you most value?'

'... Well, the chair is more expensive, obviously.'

'That's not what I'm asking.' I gently brought the shovel down, caressing a cup so that it rattled like chattering teeth.

'Don't!' Fran cried.

The crowd gasped.

'I'm asking,' I repeated, 'what holds more worth?'

'What, what do you mean?'

'As a specialist – a well-earned position, no doubt – which piece do you, Fran O'Brian, most revere?'

'You've proven your point, Anja,' Lawrence said. 'Fran, don't say a word!'

Fran, now looking perturbed and emboldened, turned to him. 'Why shouldn't I give her my opinion? After all,' she turned back to me, 'Anja drove all this way to hear it.' She displayed the same cunning smile she had months ago when I'd stepped into my office and found her sitting at my desk. 'It's the Susie Cooper, obviously! It's such a cute set.'

'*Fooool!*' screamed Lawrence.

'Wrong answer,' I said, striking the tea set with my shovel. It smashed into a million pieces that flew over Fran and into the crowd.

I snatched up my chair and ran like lightning.

I drove for an hour through the city, into the redbrick suburbs and concrete industrial landscapes. Leaving behind traffic lights and highway megastores, I passed smallholdings and sheep stations, eventually turning onto a private dirt road marked by a billboard with an elegant font. I rolled down the windows, breathing in the open air and marvelling at the beauty of the rolling hills. The sun was setting as I approached the yellow farmhouse with its wraparound verandah and blooming wisteria.

I turned off the ignition and took the chair from the back seat. Beth walked out of the house, arms crossed, her hair shorter than it had been before. We stared at one another, each of us on our own ground. Then she stepped off the verandah and came towards me.

'Before you say anything,' I began, 'I just want to apologise. I've been a shit of a friend.'

'You *look* like shit,' she said, standing next to me. 'What's with the chair?'

'I stole it … for you. An olive branch, of sorts. It's very expensive, culturally significant, one of the most exceptional pieces I've ever come across.'

She took the chair from me and ran her hands along its finely tapered legs, just as I had in a different life from underneath Mrs Hiegel.

'They're going to come after me,' I said. 'I'll likely get into a lot of trouble, but I'll tell them I destroyed it. They'll never know it's here.'

She looked back at me and shook her head with a smile. 'Thank you,' she said, and then hugged me tighter than I'd been held in a long time.

Thanks for the chair? For the honesty? It didn't matter. And that was the point: we'd always been misaligned – mortise and tenon joint was never snug. I closed my eyes and rested my head against hers. Not all had been forgiven, but some things had been restored and other things had finally ended.

'Do you see that?' Beth whispered, her arm around my shoulder as she pointed into the distance.

I scanned the horizon. 'What?'

'Over there, between the vines … There's a man, dressed in black.'

'I can't see anyone,' I said, squinting.

We stood in silence, surveying her land and the shadows cast by the bowing sun.

'Never mind,' she said after a moment, smiling to herself

then pushing loose hair behind my ear. 'Tell me more about the chair.'

I left the chair with Beth – I'd appreciate it if you kept that information to yourselves. Obviously I can't return to my shack; it's the first place they'd look. I remembered a taxi driver had once told me that this place is a kind of sanctuary – that you sirens make good listeners. And I need to tell it my way, before facts and figures dull the finish. So I thought I'd wait it out here, if you don't mind? Can I place my head, just for a moment, in your lap? No doubt they'll soon storm the door. I've paid by credit card; it won't take them long to track. It's such a soft lap you have, so reassuring. Yes, I like it when you brush my hair. I can hear the ocean from here, and I *am* ready to face the consequences, but just let me rest a little, before the hammer falls.

She mirrors his movements from behind a bush. One step, two steps. He stops and spins around; she freezes, crouches low. He scans the land and calls her name, but she does not answer. When he turns again with dorsum now towards her, she leaps through the air and jostles with his shoulders. It's a fine leap – he stumbles – but there's no malice in it. She's learned what happens when she treats them as prey, when her paw is weighted and her jaw clenched. She understands, now, that they are in command and that the length of her restraints run parallel to her behaviour: to challenge them is to be tied down, to eat and shit in place. But to submit, to respect, is to have full rein of the enclosure, to traverse its electrified boundaries and to climb its axed trees to the barbed and rusty ceiling.

He visits twice a day, when the sun rises and before it sets, bringing with him cattle, sheep, goat and deer, all cold and cleaved. Occasionally he'll let loose chickens in her enclosure, but only when he is back behind the fence. She severs one bird after another, then stores their bodies in the tin shelter he has built, snacking on them when she is bored.

She is bored most days. When she is not, it's because he has appeared unexpectedly. They'll wrestle and play ball, which often ends with her flopping herself onto him and letting him rub her neck and stomach. She'll close her eyes like a flirt and rumble her chest, because it feels good and the vibrations soothe them both.

If she's lucky, he'll fit her harness and walk her down to the sea. They swim together at a private cove, her lead attached to his waist. She's learned the hard way not to drink the water and has caught more than one gummy shark that stalks the shore's edge, attracted by spider crabs that bury themselves in the fertile sand surrounding the wetlands.

She's relieved when it's the beach he takes her to. Other times, it's the township – to be adorned in a sash and marched alongside him and others, hundreds of others, where noises are startling and men pull her tail.

It's been a while since she was last paraded, though, and this morning when he arrives, his scent has changed. He smells of oil, rot, vinegar and cortisol – like the released chickens about to take flight. She doesn't trust this smell and pulls away from his embrace. It's soon forgotten, though, when he drags from his car a squealing pig. The prey rounds the enclosure twice before she has its neck between her jaws. And it's too round, too fat, too tempting to leave for later, so she slices open the belly and pushes her head inside the rib cage to the warm, still-pulsing organs. When she has finished eating, she lies down in the fading sun and cleans the blood from her paws and face.

He approaches with bowed head and rounded shoulders, but she's too well fed to interpret the posture and welcomes his lap and a firm hand behind her ears. He taps at her ticked fur and traces his fingers along the black rings of her eyes that like tears cascade down her muzzle, before he rests something cold against her temple.

And then she is up, up and away. She can see him in the cage, crouched and sobbing, and she can see this strange land, with its thick, tangled bush and ash-coloured sand breaking at the vast, bracing ocean – there's a lifetime of ocean – until it's her old land of undulating red soil and watchful mountain peaks, and cubs – her cubs, fully grown with offspring of their own, nipping and somersaulting beneath the midday shade of a Joshua tree; her trusted universal order has returned. And then, drifting into mythology and fable, she sees no more, for narrative is a human concept and has nothing to do with the wild.

Acknowledgements

The manuscript was written over three years on Hydra and Crete, and in Melbourne and Johannesburg. I'd like to thank my international hosts – Nikos and Dora on Crete, Eleni on Hydra, and Helene and Lucy in Joburg – for providing beautiful, inspiring spaces for me to live and work.

The spine of the manuscript was written during my Cretan Mudhouse Residency, made possible by the founders Varvara Liakounakou and Jenny Carolin. Their exceptional program, set amongst the ruins of a mountain town, allows artists to explore and challenge their creativity in a unique and enchanting environment. My time at Mudhouse would not have been as rewarding were it not for the friendship, support and encouragement of my fellow residents – thank you for sharing your work, ideas and bottles of Raki.

A similarly supportive environment was to be found in Antoni Jach's Masterclass XVII. Antoni's writing tools and guidance were invaluable to progressing the manuscript.

On completion, the manuscript was assessed by Angela Meyer of Meyer Literary. Angela's careful reading, informed and considered insights ensured the manuscript was ready to take its first steps into the world. I cannot thank Angela enough.

Thanks to my agent, Martin Shaw, for championing this offbeat book and suggesting its far better title; my Transit Lounge Publisher, Barry Scott, for his enthusiasm for *Hydra* and making my dreams come true; and my editor, Kate Goldsworthy, whose exceptional eye for detail and continuity, refined and elevated the manuscript.

Thanks to my mother, Julie Howell, for her constant encouragement and fierce proofreading skills; my love and sounding board, Simon Whyte, for kicking me out of bed at 5am and offering valuable character assessment; my father, Carl Howell, for feeding my imagination; and my *Gargouille* partner, Sarah Wreford, for holding my hand as we ventured blindly into the literary landscape. Alexis Drevikovsky and the old crew at Writers Victoria, what a treat it was working with such supportive literary ladies. I would never have written a word had not my therapist, Claire Desmond, exorcised some demons. Thanks to the Australian Institute of Interpreters and Translators, Maria Meselidis and Sandra Marks for small but vital information. And lastly, Sos – much more than just a cat.